Science Skills:

      age 11–14

Pupil data sheets

Concept maps

Reading for information

Working with line graphs

Practical work

Compounds and formulae

Teresa Burrell

The **Association**
for **Science Education**

First published 2008.Reprinted 2009.

The Association for Science Education
College Lane, Hatfield, Hertfordshire AL10 9AA

Designed by Cameron Buxton

Printed by Ashford Press Ltd

Science Skills:

     age 11–14

Introduction

Who is this book for?

This resource is for pupils age 11-14 and aims to help them develop confidence in some of the skills that underpin good science learning and expression of ideas.

The activities could be used as part of an enrichment or support programme because *Science Skills: age 11–14* aims to develop topic areas in small chunks using a simple style and with limited information per page. Pupils will quickly become familiar with the 'top tips' where snippets of help and reminders are pointed out.

This book is relevant to the National Curricula for England and Wales and is ideal for use as starter or plenary activities. Teachers and students of other curricula will find much useful material relevant to their courses.

The five skills sections

Science Skills: age 11–14 covers five skill areas.
- Concept mapping
- Reading for information
- Working with line graphs
- Practical work – planning, carrying out and reporting experiments
- Working with compounds and formulae

Pupil portfolios

Trials with *Science Skills: age 11–14* have shown that the material is particularly useful in raising performance with middle and lower achievers. Teachers have found that providing pupils with a folder, kept in class, into which they build their own personal reference library is successful. Taken through to 14-16 the folder provides an outstanding reference tool for helping pupils to complete regular tasks such as practical reports and assessment tasks.

Pupils are encouraged to look after their own files by completing their own contents page as well as ongoing 'open pages' such as 'Chemical formulae'.

Information sheets at the front of the file can be adapted for use by individual schools. These give each pupil clear guidelines regarding faculty requirements, and are supported by a set of valuable data sheets, such as a copy of the Periodic Table and pH scale. All the worksheets in this book are available on the CD as Word documents that you can edit to suit your pupils. It is suggested that pupils receive the worksheets as they progress through their science course.

Science Skills

Where does the book start?

Science Skills: age 11–14 assumes that pupils are not starting from scratch and that they have some previous knowledge and experience of science, carrying out practical work and reporting their findings. However, it does not assume that they are confident with these skills. For this reason you will find that basic points are recapped, with the tasks developed to help reinforce knowledge and confidence.

Science Skills: age 11–14 complements the AKSIS (ASE-King's Science Investigations in Schools) publications *Getting to Grips with Graphs* and *Developing Understanding in Scientific Enquiry* in its aim to get pupils to develop thinking strategies and good practice that they will later rely on and find invaluable in moving forward as scientists. Pupils who have successfully worked through the skills file have shown greater independence in their learning and developed a higher degree of confidence.

Where do I start?

Where you choose to start is completely up to you and the needs of your pupils, but you will find that the ideas in each area are sequential. Whilst some pupils will be able to work through sections on their own, others will need further support and encouragement.

You will find formative assessments for each section that will help you determine the right starting point for each learner. The book also contains post-assessment tasks to help determine progress.

Placing concept maps as the first topic provides a good link from work done in primary schools and gives pupils something they are familiar with as a starting point. This section is an introduction to concept mapping and one that pupils really like – once they know they can add colour, images, notes etc. they start to express and enjoy themselves, which in turn has led to more creative learning. There are no particular right or wrong ways to produce a concept map and there are some excellent resources already available if you want to take this further.

The aim of the 'Reading for information' section is to get pupils to slow down and read more carefully – many students lose marks in tests simply because they do not read carefully enough.

Practical work is not specified as it makes sense that you use experiments falling within the context of the current learning topic. Resources are included on the 'Resources' page that you should be aware off when planning science investigations and creating risk assessments.

The 'Science laboratory health and safety rules' on page 1.3 are a pupil friendly version of more complicated and detailed notes that you can find in resources produced for the teacher. The rules on page 1.3 could form the basis of a discussion about safeguards and how useful pupils think these rules are. A blank page (page 1.4) is also provided so that together a class can produce their own set of safety guidelines.

Using ICT and print resources

You may choose to allow pupils to have access to the *Science Skills: age 11–14* book electronically by means of the enclosed CD. You could also choose to present some of the skills on the interactive whiteboard and make some of the skills learning part of a whole class activity.

You may also like to print some of the data sheets from the front of the book as display posters for your teaching room, or you may be inspired to create your own.

What this book isn't

This book is not a traditional textbook, it is more of a workbook. In itself it is not explicitly about the scientific knowledge nor is it the sole answer to how pupils can do better in science – however, it will help! As you know yourself, positive and constructive feedback are just as essential to promoting progress and form an integral part of the skills learning process. Try to ask pupils to apply this learning throughout their science class work and use your knowledge of their skills learning to inform your marking and feedback.

Finally...

You know your pupils best – you know what they will respond to and how they will learn most effectively – you are the one who is able to use this resource to its best potential using your own professional expertise.

I hope this guide helps you and that you enjoy using it with your pupils.

Teresa Burrell

2008

Resources

This is by no means an exhaustive list but includes resources that I have found extremely useful in informing myself and using in the classroom. I am sure you will have your own tried and tested favourites that you will want to add to this list.

Concept mapping

- Tony Buzan, inventor of the Mindmap, official website. **http://www.buzanworld.com/** Provides a link to publications including *Mindmaps for Kids* published by Harper Collins (ISBN 0007151330)

- SmartIdeas concept mapping software from Smart Technologies **http://www2.smarttech.com/st/en-US/Products/SMART+Ideas/**

Reading for information

- *Science web reader* – Biology, published by Nelson Thornes (ISBN 978-0174387374)
- *Science web reader* – Chemistry, published by Nelson Thornes (ISBN 978-0174387503)
- *Science web reader* – Physics, published by Nelson Thornes (ISBN 978-0174387510)

Working with line graphs

- *AKSIS – Getting to grips with graphs* published by ASE (ISBN 978 0 86357302 6)

Practical work

- CLEAPSS – advisory service supporting science and technology in schools and colleges throughout the United Kingdom (for Scotland see below). **http://www.cleapss.org.uk/**

- SSERC – advisory service supporting science and technology in schools and colleges in Scotland. **http://www.sserc.org.uk/public/**

- *Safeguards in the School Laboratory* (11th edition) published by ASE (ISBN 978 0 86357408 5)

- *Topics in Safety* (3rd edition) published by ASE (ISBN 978 0 86357316 3)

- The accompanying CD-ROM includes a PDF of the Laboratory rules found in *Safeguards in the School Laboratory*.

Working with compounds and formulas

- Top science 'elements' produced by ASE **http://sycd.co.uk/only_connect/startfil/home.htm**

- Formula cards and Chemical equations matching activities produced by ASE **http://sycd.co.uk/aka_science/explore/fun_size.htm**

Contents

Introduction

Contents

Science Skills

Science Skills

6 Practical work – planning, carrying out and reporting experiments

Science Skills

Science Skills

Science Skills:

 age 11–14

Science Skills:
age 11–14

Contents	Date	Page number

Science lab health and safety rules

1   Only enter a lab when told to do so by your teacher.

2   Tell your teacher if you spill any chemicals or damage apparatus.

3   Tie back hair and tuck in loose clothing before starting an experiment.

4   No eating, drinking or chewing gum in the lab.

5   Wear eye protection (goggles) from the start until the last person has finished when there is a hazard or as instructed.

6   Do not run in the lab.

7   Put bags and coats in a safe place before starting practical work.

8   Never leave a Bunsen burner unattended.

9   Before you start read all instructions carefully. Follow instructions, and if you are not sure what to do, ask the teacher.

10 Keep your work space clean, clear and tidy.

1.3

Science lab health and safety rules

 # Presenting your work

✓ Write in blue or black pen. Use a different colour to highlight key words and ideas.

✓ Make sure each new piece of work has a date, title and learning objective.

✓ Start each new sentence with a capital letter and finish it with a full stop. If your sentence is a question, end it with a question mark.

✓ Write neatly and keep work neat and tidy so that you have a good exercise book to revise from.

✓ Underline titles using a ruler.

✓ Draw all straight lines using a ruler.

✓ Complete diagrams and drawings in pencil.

✓ Notes may be written in bullet points, just like this list.

✓ Do not graffiti on or in your exercise book.

✓ Stick in any loose worksheets.

Marking

- Expect your exercise book to be marked about once every fortnight.

- You will receive an **EFFORT GRADE**

  + Excellent work

  o Satisfactory work

  - Unsatisfactory work – you should work with your teacher to make improvements.

- Please read comments carefully and aim to make improvements.

- At the end of each topic you will receive a National Curriculum Science Level.

Periodic Table of the Elements

Group 1	Group 2											Group 3	Group 4	Group 5	Group 6	Group 7	Group 0
1 **H** 1 Hydrogen																	4 **He** 2 Helium
7 **Li** 3 Lithium	9 **Be** 4 Beryllium											11 **B** 5 Boron	12 **C** 6 Carbon	14 **N** 7 Nitrogen	16 **O** 8 Oxygen	19 **F** 9 Fluorine	20 **Ne** 10 Neon
23 **Na** 11 Sodium	24 **Mg** 12 Magnesium											27 **Al** 13 Aluminium	28 **Si** 14 Silicon	31 **P** 15 Phosphorus	32 **S** 16 Sulphur	35.5 **Cl** 17 Chlorine	40 **Ar** 18 Argon
39 **K** 19 Potassium	40 **Ca** 20 Calcium	45 **Sc** 21 Scandium	48 **Ti** 22 Titanium	51 **V** 23 Vanadium	52 **Cr** 24 Chromium	55 **Mn** 25 Mangenese	56 **Fe** 26 Iron	59 **Co** 27 Cobalt	59 **Ni** 28 Nickel	64 **Cu** 29 Copper	65 **Zn** 30 Zinc	70 **Ga** 31 Gallium	73 **Ge** 32 Germanium	75 **As** 33 Arsenic	79 **Se** 34 Selenium	80 **Br** 35 Bromine	84 **Kr** 36 Krypton
85 **Rb** 37 Rubidium	88 **Sr** 38 Strontium	89 **Y** 39 Yttrium	91 **Zr** 40 Zirconium	93 **Nb** 41 Niobium	96 **Mo** 42 Molybdenum	98 **Tc** 43 Technetium	101 **Ru** 44 Ruthenium	103 **Rh** 45 Rhodium	106 **Pd** 46 Palladium	108 **Ag** 47 Silver	112 **Cd** 48 Cadmium	115 **In** 49 Indium	119 **Sn** 50 Tin	122 **Sb** 51 Antimony	128 **Te** 52 Tellurium	127 **I** 53 Iodine	131 **Xe** 54 Xenon
133 **Cs** 55 Caesium	137 **Ba** 56 Barium	139 **La** 57 Lanthanum	178 **Hf** 72 Hafnium	181 **Ta** 73 Tantalum	184 **W** 74 Tungsten	186 **Re** 75 Rhenium	190 **Os** 76 Osmium	192 **Ir** 77 Iridium	195 **Pt** 78 Platinum	197 **Au** 79 Gold	201 **Hg** 80 Mercury	204 **Tl** 81 Thallium	207 **Pb** 82 Lead	209 **Bi** 83 Bismuth	210 **Po** 84 Polonium	210 **At** 85 Astatine	222 **Rn** 86 Radon
223 **Fr** 37 Francium	226 **Ra** 88 Radium	227 **Ac** 89 Actinium															

2.1

pH chart

Increasing acidity	1	**Battery acid**
	2	
	3	**Lemon juice**
	4	Vinegar
	5	Washing up liquid
	6	
Neutral	7	Milk
	8	
	9	Kitchen cleaner
	10	
	11	**Ammonia**
	12	
Increasing alkalinity	13	**Dilute sodium hydroxide**
	14	

1	2	3	4	5	6	7	8	9	10	11	12	13	14
Red		Orange		Yellow		Green					Blue	Purple	

The pH and colours given by Universal Indicator

2.2

Science Skills

Chemical formulae

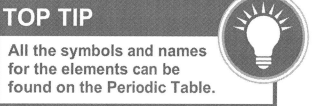
Name of chemical	Chemical formula
Carbon dioxide	CO_2
Carbon monoxide	CO
Water	H_2O
Ammonia	NH_3
Glucose (a sugar)	$C_6H_{12}O_6$
Sodium chloride (common salt)	$NaCl$
Hydrochloric acid	HCl
Sulfuric acid	H_2SO_4
Nitric acid	HNO_3
Sodium hydroxide	$NaOH$
Potassium hydroxide	KOH
Calcium carbonate (chalk)	$CaCO_3$
Sulfur dioxide (a greenhouse gas)	SO_2
Nitrogen dioxide (a pollutant from car fumes)	NO_2
Hydrogen gas	H_2
Oxygen gas	O_2
Nitrogen gas	N_2

Chemical formulae – continued

Add more as you learn them

Name of chemical	Chemical formula

Top tips

The science test

Things to remember when tackling science questions

1 Read the entire question carefully or you may miss important information.

2 Make sure you understand what the question is asking. Even if a picture or diagram is familiar the question might not be the one you expect.

3 You can sometimes add a drawing to help answer a question.

4 Don't be put off if you find a question on something you have not covered in lesson. This sort of question is not testing what you can remember but whether you can read and make sense of some new information on a science topic you have studied.

5 Always try to use scientific words accurately. It may not be crucial to spell all the words entirely correctly but you should know when and how to use them.

6 Don't forget to include units such as ^{o}C, g, s (seconds), N, etc. when needed. In science, numbers without units usually have no meaning.

7 Arrows in food webs or on light rays must point in the correct direction. Use a ruler and put in arrows to show this.

Top tips

Answering questions in tests

Getting maximum marks!

Whether you like it or not you are often assessed on how good your learning is by completing a test. Many pupils make simple mistakes and lose marks – don't let that be you.

These tips might help you to improve!

- How many marks is the answer worth? If it is worth two points you need to give two bits of information.

- Check to see whether you need to write in sentences or if you can write one word answers instead.

- Try to use key scientific words in answers.

- Write clearly – the marker cannot give the marks if they cannot read your answer!

- Read questions carefully. Make sure you know what you are being asked.

- If you get stuck on a question, move on and come back to it later.

- Remember to include units and show 'working out' for any calculations you are asked to do.

- Use good English and proper words – not slang!

Top tips

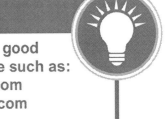
TOP TIP

Always use a good
search engine such as:
www.yahoo.com
www.google.com

Successful Internet searches

Refining your Internet searches can improve your chances of finding the
information you really want and stop you wasting time.

Try these techniques.

Quotes (" ")

Top and tail the phrase / words you are looking for with
quote marks.
The search engine looks for the whole phrase.

Plus (+)

Add a plus sign (+) directly in front of a word.
A search for *+reactions* and *+metals* would return a list of sites
where you could find out about reactions of metals.
If you search on *+reactions of metals*, you would receive a list
of reactions websites, but not necessarily metal reactions.

Minus (-)

Adding a minus sign (-) in front of a word tells the search
engine to ignore that word.
A search on *+reactions +metals - acids* would return sites on
reactions of metals, but not acids.

Wildcard character (*)

Using * in front of a word allows you to search on variations of a
word, or both singular and plural forms.

Top tips

Remember the order of the planets

It can be easy to remember things if you use a mnemonic – that's where you use the first letter of each thing you need to remember, but make up your own phrase to go with it.

For example, you could remember the order of the major planets using this phrase.

Mystery	**Mercury**
Vampire	**Venus**
Entertained	**Earth**
Marvellous	**Mars**
Jazz	**Jupiter**
Singer	**Saturn**
Uncle	**Uranus**
Neville	**Neptune**

TOP TIP

You can use this technique to help you remember lots of things. Make your phrase memorable – even add a picture.

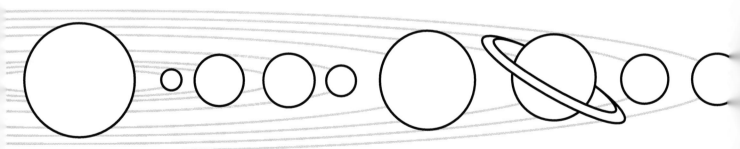

2.8

 Units

Length	millimetres	mm
	centimetres	cm
	metres	m

| Area | centimetres squared | cm^2 |
| | metres squared | m^2 |

| Volume | cubic centimetres | cm^3 |
| | cubic metres | m^3 |

| Volume | litres | l |

| Mass | grams / kilograms | g / kg |

| Force | newton | N |

| Temperature | degrees Celsius | °C |

| Speed | kilometres per hour | km/h |

TOP TIP

Use a ruler for drawing and measuring all straight lines

°C
50
45
40
35
30
25
20
15
10
5
0
-5
-10
-15

 # Hazard symbols

Match the symbol to its correct meaning.

Toxic

Explosive

Harmful / irritant

Dangerous for environment

Highly flammable

Oxidising

Corrosive

2.10

Using hazard symbols

Use your hazard symbols fact sheet to help identify the dangers of some chemicals.

Your teacher will now show you five chemicals:

Name of chemical	Hazard symbol on bottle

1   What hazard symbol would you expect to see on a bottle for the following?

    a   Sulfuric acid _____

    b   Iodine _____

    c   Mercury _____

2   Which symbol would represent chemicals in the laboratory that have these effects?

Kills fish in rivers	Makes your eyes water	Burns a hole in the desk	Causes an explosion in a fume cupboard	Causes holes in shoes

The Bunsen burner

Remind yourself how to use a Bunsen burner safely.

1 Label the parts of the Bunsen burner on the diagram below.

Use these words for your labels:

Base
Collar
Chimney
Air hole
Rubber tube to gas

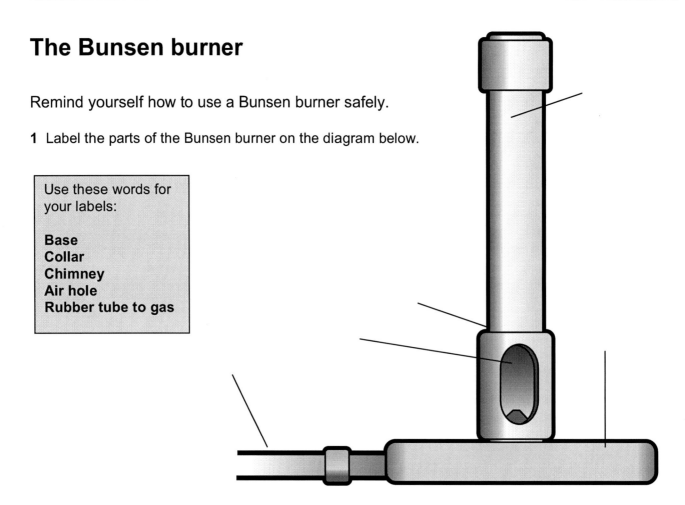

2 Complete these sentences by crossing out the wrong word.

When you light the Bunsen burner the air hole should be **open / closed**.

A **blue / green / yellow** flame will appear. When you open the air hole the flame will get **colder / hotter**.

3 Answer these questions as a group.

a How do you make the flame hotter?

_____

b Which is the hottest part of the flame?

_____

c Why does the burner have a large, heavy base?

_____

d Where does gas enter the Bunsen burner?

_____

2.12e

The Bunsen burner

Remind yourself how to use a Bunsen burner safely.

1 Label the parts of the Bunsen burner on the diagram below.

2 Complete these sentences.

When you light the Bunsen burner the air hole should be _____ .

A _____ flame will appear. When you open the air hole the flame will get

_____ .

3 Answer these questions.

    a How do you make the flame hotter?

    _____

    b Which is the hottest part of the flame?

    _____

    c Why does the burner have a large, heavy base?

    _____

    d Where does gas enter the Bunsen burner?

    _____

2.12h

Using the microscope

Parts of a microscope

Use the words in the text box to help you label the parts of a light microscope and answer the questions.

Handle

Focussing knob

Eyepiece lens

Objective lens

Stage

Tube

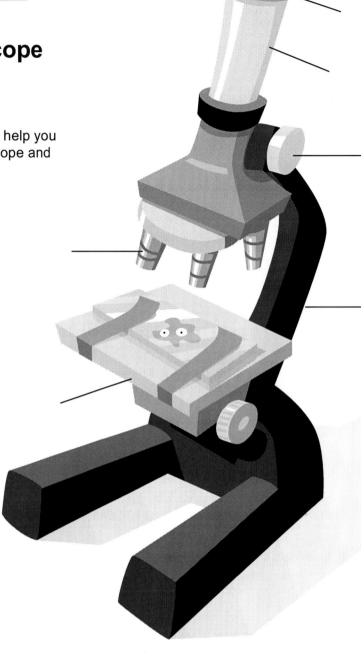

The microscope you are using might look slightly different to the one in the picture. Some have a built-in light, but others have a mirror that you have to move to reflect daylight into the lens.

1   Which two pieces of the microscope should you never touch?

_____

2   Which part of the microscope would you place your slide on?

_____

3   Which part do you use to carry the microscope?

_____

Life reactions

Respiration

glucose + oxygen ➡ carbon dioxide + water

All living things respire.

> Respiration happens inside every living cell. It releases the energy needed for living.

Photosynthesis

carbon dioxide + water ➡ glucose + oxygen

Only green plants in the light photosynthesise.

> Photosynthesis and respiration are closely linked reactions – that's why the balance between plants and animals is so important.

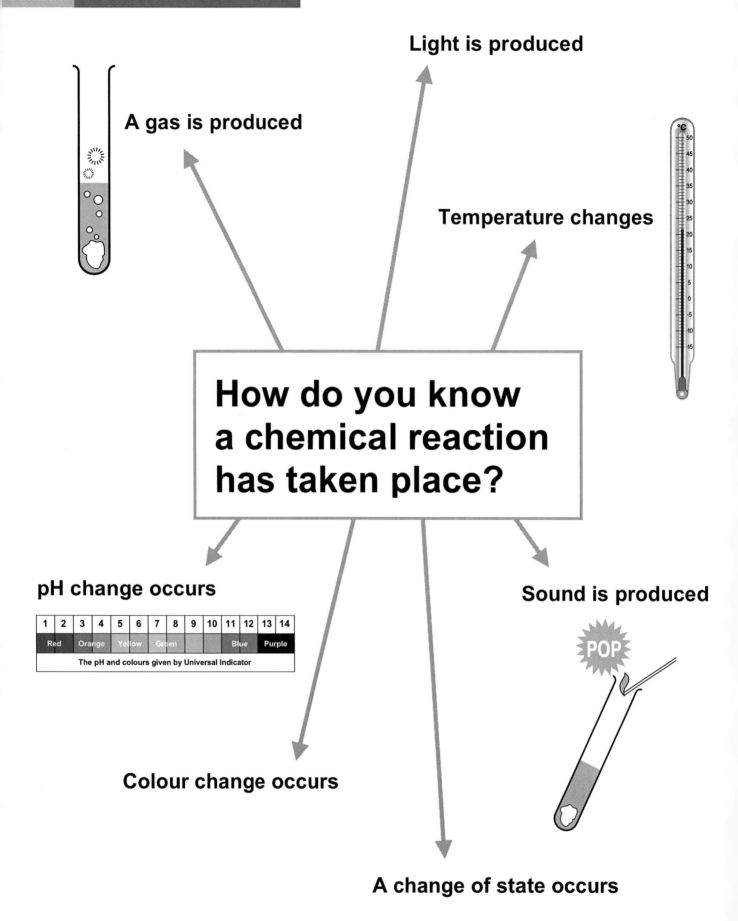

A gas is produced

Light is produced

Temperature changes

How do you know a chemical reaction has taken place?

pH change occurs

1	2	3	4	5	6	7	8	9	10	11	12	13	14
Red		Orange		Yellow		Green					Blue		Purple

The pH and colours given by Universal Indicator

Sound is produced

POP

Colour change occurs

A change of state occurs

Helpful formulae

You often need to work out things in science using your maths skills.
Here are some useful equations to refer to.

(NC Level 4 / 5)

average speed (m/s) = $\dfrac{\text{distance travelled (m)}}{\text{time taken (s)}}$

(NC Level 5)

The law of reflection states:

the angle of incidence (i) = the angle of reflection (r)

work = force (N) x distance (m)   units: newton metre (Nm)

(NC Level 6)

Photosynthesis

carbon dioxide + water → glucose + oxygen (light energy needed)

Respiration

oxygen + glucose → carbon dioxide + water + energy

(NC Level 7)

pressure (N/m^2) = $\dfrac{\text{force (N)}}{\text{area (m}^2)}$

TOP TIP

Remember to show how you worked out the answer.

Name that salt

This information sheet will show you how to work out the name of a salt formed in a reaction.

Salts are formed in lots of reactions.

The name of the salt depends on the acid used in the reaction.

Hydrochloric acid makes chlorides

Sulfuric acid makes sulfates

Nitric acid makes nitrates

For example:

hydrochloric acid + iron → iron **chloride** + hydrogen

sulfuric acid + sodium hydroxide → sodium **sulfate** + water

Notice how the metal that is used becomes the first part of the salt name.

hydrochloric acid + **iron** → **iron** chloride + hydrogen

sulfuric acid + **sodium** hydroxide → **sodium** sulfate + water

Writing formulae data sheet

Formulae, such as CO_2 and H_2O are a short-hand way of writing down a chemical. With a few simple rules and some practice, writing formulae is easy to master.

Each element has a value or valency. This value depends on where you find the element in the Periodic Table.

Group	1	2				3	4	5	6	7	0
				H							He
	Li	Be				B	C	N	O	F	Ne
	Na	Mg				Al	Si	P	S	Cl	Ar
	K	Ca		Transition Metals		Ga	Ge	As	Se	Br	Kr
	Rb	Sr				In	Sn	Sb	Te	I	Xe
	Cs	Ba				Tl	Pb	Bi	Po	At	Rn
	Fr	Ra									

To keep it simple at this stage we can say:

Group 1 elements have a value of +1.

Group 2 elements have a value of +2.

Group 3 elements have a value of +3.

Group 4 elements have a value of +4 or -4.

Group 5 elements have a value of -3.

Group 6 elements have a value of -2.

Group 7 elements have a value of -1.

Hydrogen has a value of +1.

Most transition metals have a value of +2. Silver is +1.
Some can have more than one value, e.g. iron is +2 or +3.

Two or more atoms of different elements combine to form chemical groups, which also have values (valencies).

Sulfate has a value of -2 (SO_4^{2-})

Nitrate has a value of -1 (NO_3^-)

Carbonate has a value of -2 (CO_3^{2-})

Hydroxide has a value of -1 (OH^-)

You will need this information later on.

> The word 'group' is used in two different ways. We use it for a Group in the Periodic Table and for a chemical group of combined atoms

Concept mapping

Mini concept maps

Concept maps can be used for many things including linking ideas and topics together, making learning connections and summarising your knowledge. There are lots of different ways of making concept maps – the examples on the next two pages give some hints.

Complete this mini concept map by writing link ideas on the arrows.

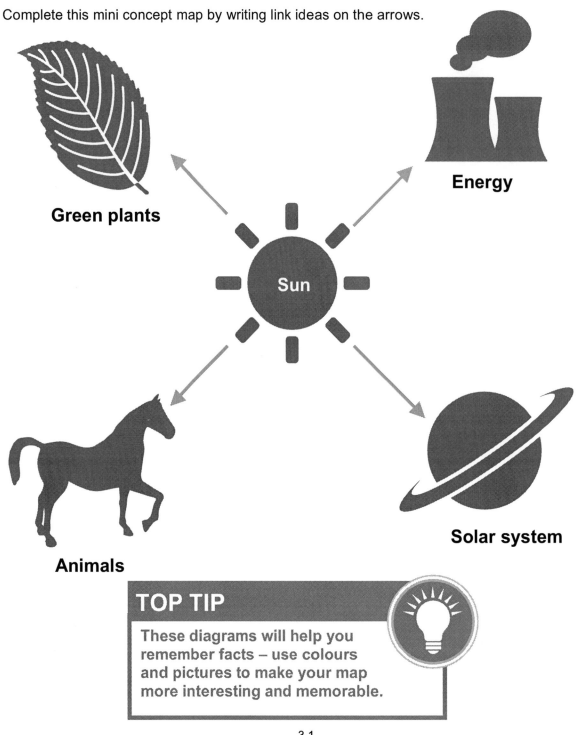

Green plants

Energy

Sun

Animals

Solar system

TOP TIP

These diagrams will help you remember facts – use colours and pictures to make your map more interesting and memorable.

3.1

Concept maps 1

Using concept maps reduces writing and helps you to build up a clearer picture about how ideas are linked together.

You can draw concept maps to show connections between all sorts of things. Here is just one example showing connections between the processes involved in respiration. Again, there are lots of different ways this could have been done.

Main theme – Respiration in cells

Connect with – energy release, respiration, chemical reaction, movement, glucose, oxygen, lungs, breathing.

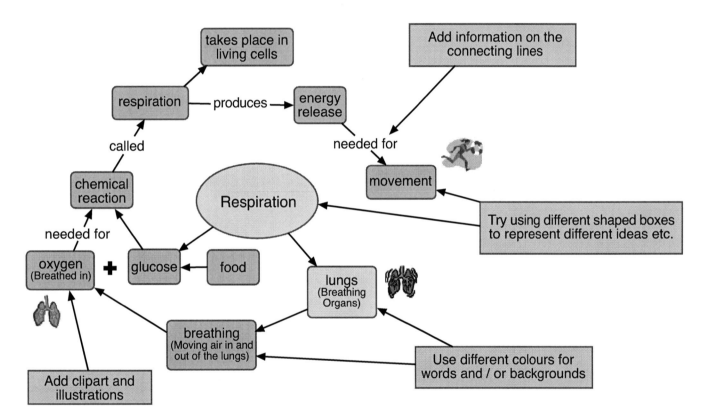

Your go!

Draw a concept map using the following words. Try to add other words and connections if you can.

Main theme – Heart

Connect with – blood, pump, vessel, muscle, circulatory system, skeletal system, movement, arteries, veins, oxygen, carbon dioxide.

Concept maps 1

Self-assessment

How well did you get on with creating a concept map about the heart?

Assess your map honestly using the grid below. Remember there are lots of different ways to make successful concept maps. If you think you have done something really well in your map you should say so.

Question	Your response	Suggestions for improvement
Do you have a clear title? OR, Is it clear what your concept map is about?		Put the title in a larger box. Increase the size of the title, or colour it differently to make it stand out.
Have you made logical links from the title to other ideas / words? How did you decide what to link to first?		Link to the most important points first.
How have you physically linked ideas together, i.e. arrow, symbol, line? Why did you choose this method?		
Have you used different letter sizes, capital letters and colours on your concept map? Where did you use them and why did you use them?		Different size letters and colours can make points stand out or group the ideas together.
Did you choose to put information on the links between boxes? Do you think this helps to understand the map?		Consider adding a few words on links to make the relationship between the boxes clearer.
Has the concept map helped you to link ideas together? Does it help you to remember and learn?		

Concept maps 2

Now you have had a chance to build a concept map and point out how well you did.

Below is a concept map created by another student on the topic of acids and alkalis.

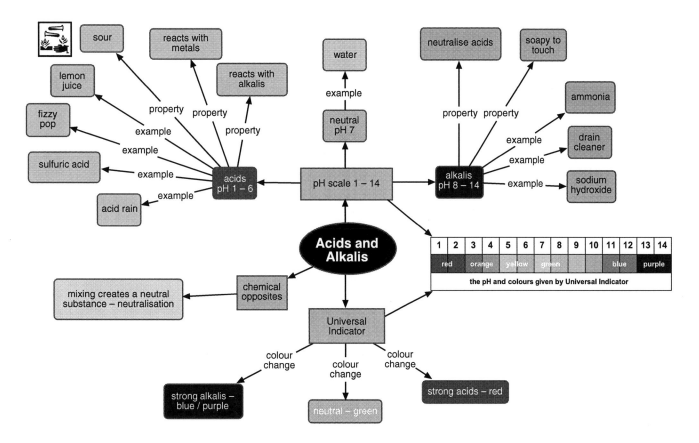

How well do you think she did?

1 Why do you think the student drew a concept map? Underline the reasons you think the student gave.

Saved time

Help me to remember – I can remember pictures better than lots of writing

Did not have to write as much

I could add pictures – they help me to remember

Helped me to put all the ideas about acids and alkalis together in one place

Continued

2 Highlight these parts of the map.

1. Clear title – I know what the concept map is about.	2. The boxes are linked clearly.	3. Different colours / shades / shaped boxes are used.
4. Not too much text in each box – points still clear.	5. Illustrations. (Do you think they help?)	6. Well organised and laid out.

3 Suggest three things the student could do to improve the next concept map she draws.

_____

_____

_____

Concept maps 3

Now you have had a chance to build a concept map and point out how well you did.
Below is a concept map created by another student on the topic of acids and alkalis.

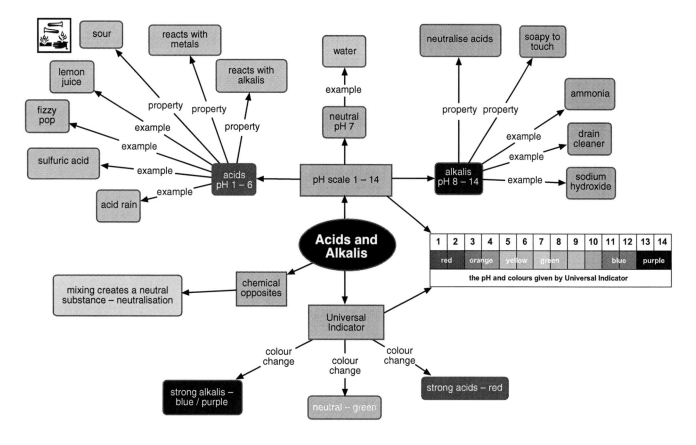

1   Why do you think the student drew a concept map?

_____

2   Briefly state five things about the concept map that you think are good or that you like.
    Ring them on the map.

_____

_____

_____

_____

3   Suggest three things the student could do to improve the next concept map she draws.

_____

_____

_____

Concept maps 3

Now you have seen a few concept maps, have a go at creating your own – it doesn't matter where you start. Get a large piece of paper and start making connections.

Physical changes

Draw a concept map using these words. Try to add other connections and words if you can.

Main theme – Physical change

Connect with – solute, solvent, solution, filtrate, residue, filtration, evaporation, chromatography, soluble, simple distillation, insoluble, crystallisation, mixture.

Magnetism

Draw a concept map using these words. Try to add other connections and words if you can.

Main theme – Magnetism

Connect with – bar magnet, north pole, south pole, core, solenoid, magnetic field, current, voltage, uses of a bar magnet, uses of electromagnets.

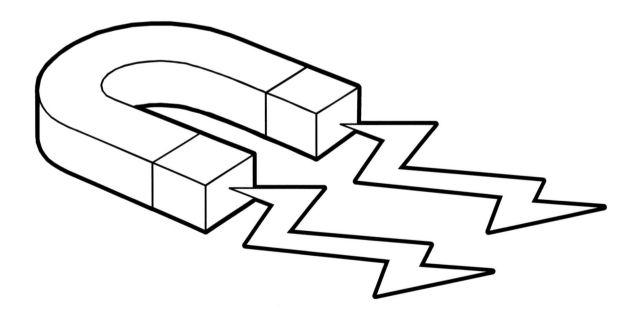

Reading for information

Self-assessment

1
I can read information from a diagram or illustration.

Practice by trying 'Reading for information 1' and 'Reading for information 2'.

2
I can read a small amount of text (half page of A4) successfully.

Practice by trying 'Reading for information 3' and 'Reading for information 6'.

3
I can read information from a line graph.

Practice by trying 'Reading for information 4'.

4
I can read information from a table.

Practice by trying 'Reading for information 5'.

5
If I am finding reading difficult I use different methods to help me.

If you want to know more see the 'Reading for information help sheet'.

6
I can read for information successfully and am ready to try a more challenging task.

Try 'Reading for information 7'.

Reading for information

Help sheet

Reading and comprehension skills are useful in most subjects, not just science. If a concept is difficult or if you are asked to read a large amount of information the following strategies should help you to understand and recall the information more readily.

Strategy 1
Make sure you have read the title – this often gives a big clue about what the piece of text is all about.

Strategy 2
Get comfortable – not so easy in a science laboratory perhaps! A quieter atmosphere helps most people to take in more information.

Strategy 3
Read the article twice. On the first reading get the general idea about the information – what is the big picture? After reading, ask yourself 'What was that about?' What questions arise and what things do you not understand.
On the second reading, read with the purpose of filling in the gaps and answering the points that you are not sure about.

Strategy 4
Look for keywords and terms. If you are reading a large section of text to find out about one or two specific things, this strategy may help you to find them more quickly. Be careful, however, as to understand what they mean still needs you to read the text carefully.

Strategy 6
Jot down one or two short sentences that summarise the ideas / facts in each paragraph. If you have to go back and look for specific pieces of information this will help you to find them, as well as build up a summary.

Strategy 5
Create your own concept map of the ideas you have been reading about – make links and connections.

These techniques can really help you if you have to read longer pieces of text, but all of the strategies can be used with any piece of reading, however small. You will find some strategies more helpful than others – pick the ones that suit the way you learn.

4.2

Reading for information 1

You are often asked to read a piece of text or look at diagrams, pictures or charts to pick out certain pieces of information. This can form an important part of research and develop your ideas and knowledge. The next few worksheets will help you to practice this skill.

Read the information about classification and use it to answer the questions.

Classification

All living things are classified. This means they are put into a group with other similar organisms.

There are five kingdoms. Every living thing belongs in one of these kingdoms.

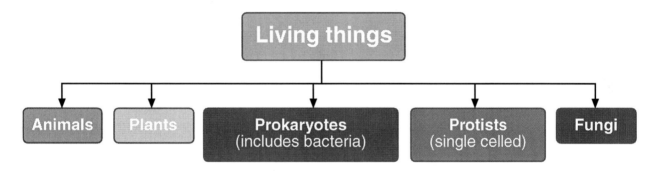

The animal kingdom is split into further groups:

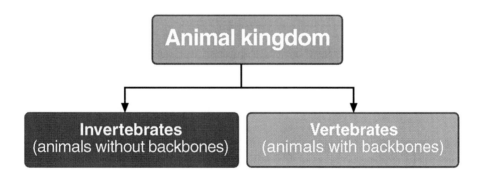

The big group **invertebrates** is a sub-kingdom of the animal kingdom. Each smaller group of invertebrates shown here is a **phylum**, e.g. molluscs.

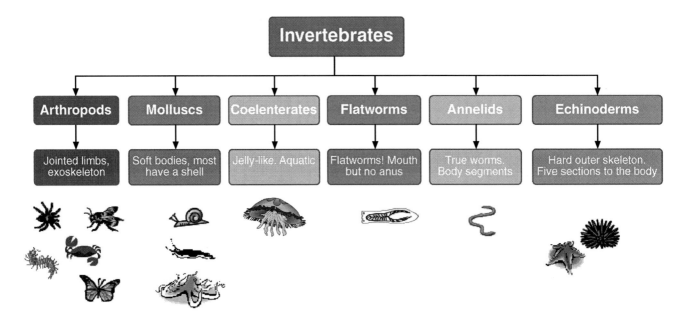

Vertebrates is the other sub-kingdom of the animal kingdom.

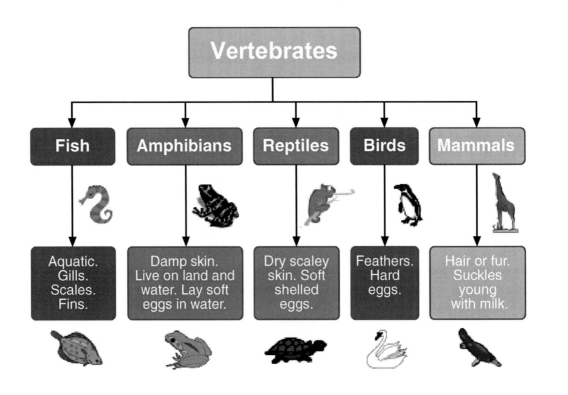

Questions

1   What is the feature shared by all vertebrates?

_____

2   How many kingdoms are there?

_____

3   What is a protist?

_____

4   Where would you find coelenterates?

_____

5   What types of animals belong in the arthropod group?

_____

6   Which two animals are shown as echinoderms?

_____

7   Which kingdom contains bacteria?

_____

8   Which group does a lizard belong to?

_____

9   If humans have hair and are able to suckle their young with milk, which group should
they be placed in?

_____

10 How can you tell an amphibian from a reptile?

_____

11   An animal is discovered with a backbone, fins and scales. How would you classify it?

_____

12 A mystery animal, lacking a backbone, but with ten jointed limbs and a hard outer body
is discovered in the ocean. How would you classify it?

_____

Reading for information 2

Here is another chance to practice your reading and comprehension skills. Perhaps this is a good time to try some of the strategies suggested on the 'Reading for information help sheet'.

Read the information about solids, liquids and gases and use it to answer the questions.

Solids, liquids and gases

There are three states of matter – solid, liquid and gas.

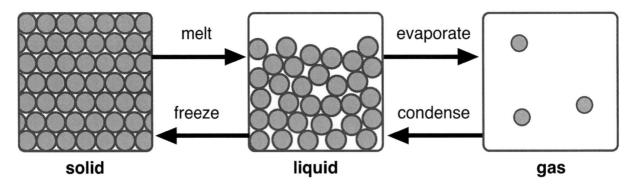

The way the particles are arranged inside a substance helps to explain its properties.

Solid	Liquid	Gas
Particles tightly packed together. Particles vibrate.	Particles close to each other and able to change places.	Particles widely spread out, with most energy. They move freely in all directions.
Cannot flow	Flow easily	
Stays in shape	Spreads out to fill the base of the container.	Fills the whole container.
Hard to compress		Easy to compress

The temperature when a solid turns into a liquid is its melting point. This is measured in degrees Celsius ($^{\circ}$C).

The boiling point is the temperature when vapour starts to form in the liquid part of the substance. Boiling liquids bubble – these bubbles contain the vapour formed in the liquid. As a liquid boils some particles have enough energy to escape the liquid and become gas. This is **evaporation**.

If a gas cools down it will condense. This is what happens in the bathroom when you take a hot bath and condensation (cooling steam) forms on the cold window or mirror.

Freezing a liquid turns it from a liquid state into a solid state, as the particles transfer energy from themselves and slow down.

A few substances, such as carbon dioxide, change from a solid straight into a gas. This is called **sublimation**.

Questions

1 How many states of matter are there?

_____

2 What happens to a solid when it is heated?

_____

3 How would you turn a liquid into a gas?

_____

4 In which state do the particles vibrate?

_____

5 In which state do the particles have most energy?

_____

6 At what temperature does a liquid turn into a gas?

_____

7 What process happens when a gas cools down and turns into a liquid?

_____

8 Which is hottest, a liquid or a gas of the same substance?

_____

9 What is happening to a liquid if it is evaporating?

_____

10 Why can a liquid flow?

_____

11 What unusual change does 'dry ice' (solid carbon dioxide) carry out as it warms up?

_____

12 What is happening to the particles in a liquid as it starts to freeze?

_____

Reading for information 3

Information is sometimes presented in text only. Read the passages carefully, take your time, and use the information to answer the questions.

Forces

Forces are pushes, pulls, bends and twists. Everything we do uses forces. Examples of forces include gravity, upthrust, drag and friction.

Weight is the force of gravity acting upon an object. On the Moon your weight will be less as the Moon has less gravitational pull than the Earth. Your mass, however, will stay the same.

Forces are measured in newtons (N), and often measured in the laboratory using a newton meter.

Sometimes forces are balanced – this means that two forces acting in opposite directions are equal. For example, when a car is moving at a steady speed the driving force is equal and opposite to the resistive forces, such as drag and friction. For a parachutist the force of gravity being equal to the drag means that she / he falls at a steady speed. To increase the speed of descent in free-fall parachutists have to change their shape and make themselves more aerodynamic. This change of shape reduces the drag forces and makes them fall more quickly. When a book rests on a table the force of gravity on the book is balanced by the upwards force of the table on the book.

Questions

1   What is a force?

_____

2   What unit is used to measure force?

_____

3   What causes weight?

_____

4   Why are you lighter on the Moon?

_____

5   Name two resistive forces.

_____

6   What are balanced forces?

_____

7   How does a parachutist in free-fall make herself go faster?

_____

Reading for information 4

Recovery rate experiment

Information can be presented in many ways. This worksheet presents data as text and in the form of a partially completed graph. You will need to use your graph and reading skills to help you answer the questions.

Questions / Tasks

Use the table and the graph on the next page to answer these questions.

Complete the graph by adding a line of best fit for each pupil.

1   What is represented by the horizontal line labelled 'Freddie'?

_____

2   What feature is missing from the graph?

_____

3   Whose heart rate was highest 0 seconds after exercise?

_____

4   What is the value of the lowest resting heart rate?

_____

5   How many minutes did it take for Nasser to recover?

_____

6   What was Nasser's heart rate at 90 seconds after completing exercise?

_____

7   Which pupil's heart rate does not return to normal after 180 seconds?

_____

8   Use the graph to predict how long it would take Tracy to recover back to her resting heart rate.

_____

9   Suggest one reason why Tracy's recovery is slower than Freddie's.

_____

_____

Three pupils carried out an experiment into recovery rate. Their aim was to find out how long it took their heart rate to get back to normal after some strenuous exercise.

Here are their results:

Pupil	Heart rate (beats per minute)				
	Normal resting rate	0 seconds after exercise	60 seconds after exercise	120 seconds after exercise	180 seconds after exercise
Freddie **X**	64	148	110	74	64
Tracy ■	80	160	140	122	100
Nasser ●	70	150	101	72	70

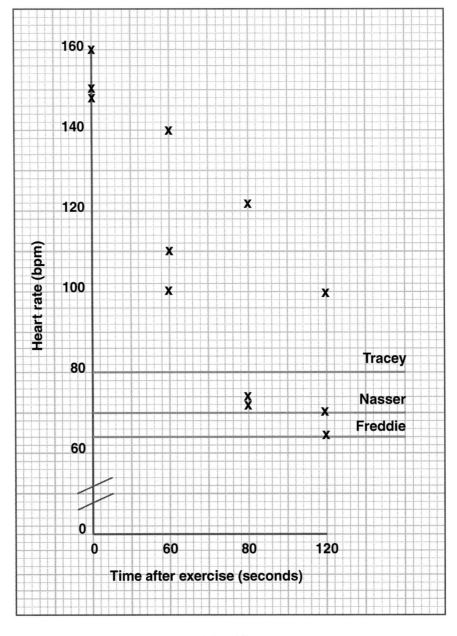

Reading for information 5

Displacement reactions

Carol investigated the reactivity of metals. She placed a small sample of a metal into a salt solution and looked for a reaction. A reaction would mean that the metal she put into the solution was more reactive than the one in solution.

These are Carol's results and conclusion:

	Iron sulfate solution	Copper sulfate solution	Calcium sulfate solution	Magnesium sulfate solution
Iron	*did not test*	**reaction**	no reaction	no reaction
Copper	no reaction	*did not test*	no reaction	no reaction
Calcium	**reaction**	**reaction**	*did not test*	**reaction**
Magnesium	**reaction**	**reaction**	no reaction	*did not test*

Copper – no reactions

Iron – 1 reaction

Magnesium – 2 reactions

Calcium – 3 reactions

Least reactive

Most reactive

Questions

1 Why did Carol not carry out a test between copper and copper sulphate?

_____

2 How would you continue this investigation to place zinc and tin into the reactivity list?

_____

_____

_____

_____

3 What would you be looking for in your results?

_____

Reading for information 6

Plants

Plants are essential to life – they make oxygen, they provide food and shelter, and are good to look at.

Unlike animals, plants are able to make their own food by photosynthesis. Energy from the Sun is transferred to and absorbed by a chemical called chlorophyll found inside the chloroplasts of plant cells. The plant takes in carbon dioxide together with water and in the presence of light produces glucose and oxygen. Energy is stored in the glucose molecules. Some of the glucose is used by the plant cells for respiration, some is stored and some is turned into other compounds needed by the plant.

It has been estimated by scientists that if the Earth suddenly lost all of its plants then all animal life would start to die off within two weeks. Without plants the oxygen supply would not be replenished and our atmosphere would quickly become over-rich with carbon dioxide; a gas that animals are not able to tolerate at high levels.

Not all plant cells contain chloroplasts, because not all plant cells photosynthesise. A good example of this is roots. Being underground root cells are not able to photosynthesise because they have no access to sunlight!

Knowing about photosynthesis has helped people to produce better crops inside greenhouses. To improve yield the lights can be kept on to lengthen daylight and additional carbon dioxide can be piped in. It is also important to keep the greenhouse warm. This is because the photosynthesis reactions rely on enzymes to speed them up. If it is too cold the reaction goes slowly, but if it is too hot the enzymes cease to function.

Green plants are found at the base of every food chain. Therefore, every living thing is also dependent on plants for their daily food. Humans eat many different plants and all parts of the plant; onions are bulbs, potatoes are swollen underground stems, asparagus is also a stem, Brussels sprouts are buds and lettuce is leaves. That's not to mention all the fruit and seeds we eat as well.

Questions

1 How do plants make their food? _____

2 Which chemicals are produced by plants in sunlight? _____

3 Which reaction will a plant use glucose for? _____

4 Where does photosynthesis take place?

_____

5 Why is temperature control an important part of photosynthesis?

_____

_____

_____

4.8

Reading for information 7

Isaac Newton

Isaac Newton (1643–1727) really was an incredible man – mathematician, philosopher, scientist, astronomer and alchemist. He was responsible for some impressive steps forward in science. His ideas have given modern day scientists an understanding of gravity, the laws of motion, planetary motion, laws concerning momentum, the reflecting telescope, knowledge of the colour spectrum, and calculus. He also suggested a theory for the origin of the stars and studied the speed of sound.

Born at Woolsthorpe Manor in Lincolnshire, Newton grew up mostly in the care of his maternal grandmother. He attended the local school before being sent as a boarder to the King's School in Grantham where his talents for mathematics and science were recognised. In June 1661 Newton went to study at Cambridge University. At this time he worked mainly on his mathematical theories. Even when the university was closed down in 1665, as a precaution against the spread of the Great Plague, Newton continued to work at home. He developed some of the most encompassing theories ever seen, which form the basis for mathematical study today.

Later on (1670–1672) Newton studied optics and was able to demonstrate that white light (the light around us) is actually made up of a spectrum of visible colours by splitting the light using a prism. He studied refraction and diffraction suggesting that light was made up of particles. Another scientist, Huygens, disagreed and suggested that light moves like a wave, an idea currently used in quantum mechanics. However, Newton's new ideas were not always well received. Robert Hooke, discoverer of cells, criticised some of Newton's ideas on light to such an extent that Newton and Hooke remained bitter enemies until Hooke's death.

Newton was also fascinated by planets and their apparent movement in the heavens. He was convinced that some force had an effect on the way planets orbited and this lead to his three 'universal laws of motion'. Newton used the Latin word for weight (*gravitas*) to describe the force at work – this later became gravity. These laws were not improved upon for more than 200 years.

There is a popular story that claims Isaac Newton was stunned into these ideas by an apple falling on his head as he daydreamed beneath the tree. Unfortunately this is not quite the case as described by John Conduitt, Newton's assistant:

"In the year 1666 he (Newton) retired again from Cambridge to his mother in Lincolnshire. Whilst he was pensively meandering in a garden it came into his thought that the power of gravity (which brought an apple from a tree to the ground) was not limited to a certain distance from Earth, but that this power must extend much further than was usually thought. Why not as high as the Moon said he to himself & if so, that must influence her motion & perhaps retain her in her orbit, whereupon he fell a calculating what would be the effect of that supposition." [Footnote1]

Newton's First Law states 'that an object at rest tends to stay at rest and that an object in uniform motion tends to stay in uniform motion unless acted upon by a net external force'. Newton's Second Law states 'that an applied force on an object equals the time rate of change of its momentum', and Newton's Third Law, probably the most familiar, states 'that for every action there is an equal and opposite reaction'.

In later life Newton wrote essays regarding interpretations of the Bible, became a Member of Parliament, Warden of the Royal Mint (1696) and then Chancellor of the Exchequer. Until his death he worked as the 'Master of the Mint' responsible for re-coining England. During that time he reformed coinage to such an extent that it added a great deal of wealth to the country and greatly pleased Her Majesty Queen Anne. Oddly it was for his work at The Mint rather than his progress in science that Queen Anne rewarded him with a knighthood in 1705.

In the last 20 years of his life Newton became more than a little eccentric – many put this down to his growing years. However, a post-mortem examination revealed that Newton's body contained a large amount of mercury – this metal and its slow poisoning effect could have explained his behaviour. Rather than being the result of any underhand event the mercury probably got into his body when Newton was studying alchemy.

The Newton Project,
http://www.newtonproject.sussex.ac.uk/prism.php?id=1
has information about Newton and his work and includes Conduitt's account of Newton's life:

http://www.newtonproject.sussex.ac.uk/texts/viewtext.php?id=THEM00165&mode=normalised

Footnote 1 – Conduitt, John. Keynes Ms. 130.4: Conduitt's account of Newton's life at Cambridge. *Newtonproject*.

Questions

1   What contributions did Isaac Newton make to scientific and mathematical understanding?

_____

_____

_____

_____

_____

2   How did an apple help Newton to come up with his ideas about gravity?

_____

_____

3   Why do you think Newton was knighted for his work at the Royal Mint rather than as a scientist or mathematician?

_____

_____

_____

Working with line graphs

Teacher introduction

This section entitled 'Working with line graphs' starts with the basics – drawing an axis and putting on a scale; it works through to extrapolating data and reading information from a graph. Many pupils really struggle with this skill in science, which is why this section appears now rather than later in the section on practical work and because graphs are used in many scientific contexts, not just with practical work.

This section does not deal with graphs in a purely mathematical context – throughout I have tried to relate graph building and interpretation as being a bit like writing and reading a storybook; there being a need to develop an outline structure and read it in a certain way to make sense of it. I have tried to explain the reasons for working on graphs in this way, put ideas into context and not make the process too mechanical. This has been with an expectation that if pupils understand why they do things in a certain way, then they are more able to use the processes correctly, develop confidence in them and apply the skills to other aspects of their learning.

Pupils should be asking questions about the way data is presented, i.e. What is a graph? How do I construct one to fit the data I have to show? How and why is it useful to me and to others? In doing this you might give pupils data, or use data collected from practical work, and ask them to display it in whichever way they think works best. They need to justify their choices but this can prove to be a very interesting exercise with pupils often presenting data clearly and successfully in ways that aren't always the most obvious choice.

There is a formative self-assessment task for pupils to carry out at the beginning of the section, with further checklists throughout. This will enable the pupil and yourself better to direct their learning to fit their needs. When the pupils have completed the 'Assess the graph' sheet you will have a record of where they should start in the section. If you have pupils who are capable of independent study let them work through the section at their own pace – possibly even set it as an extended homework exercise. There is a final assessment titled 'Drawing and using a graph' that requires pupils to use all the skills they will have developed or recalled by working through this part of the book.

You could try using each activity as a **starter** or **plenary** and supplement the pages with SAT-type practice questions for best effect. My experience with many pupils is that even with a firm grip on how to draw and interpret a line graph they can still get stuck when asked 'graph' questions on tests such as the SATs. This has been more to do with the language and context of the question, and highlighted the need for pupils to be exposed to different styles of test questions on a regular basis, and develop their skills of interpretation and question reading as well.

Working with graphs is revisited later during activities on collecting and presenting results from an experiment.

Self-assessment

Complete the task below without any help from your teacher. Don't worry about how much you can do. Just do as much as you can.

Information

Benjamin recorded how much gas was produced in two minutes for a reaction between dilute hydrochloric acid and calcium carbonate. He tried the experiment at different temperatures. The results are shown in the table.

Temperature of reaction (°C)	Volume of gas produced in 2 minutes (cm³)
0	0
10	1
20	4
30	10
40	15
50	25
60	40
70	60

The task

Draw a graph to show these results.

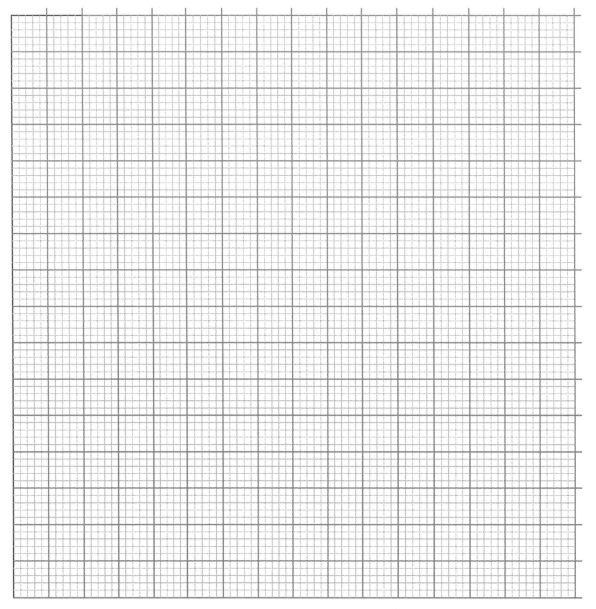

Assess the graph

You are now going to assess the graph you just drew to find out where to start in the 'Working with line graphs' series of worksheets. Your teacher will provide the worksheets you need.

Look at each statement.

Answer **YES** or **NO** and follow the instructions.

1 I know what axes are.

> **YES** – Go to question 2.
> **NO** – Go to 'Drawing axes 1'

2 I drew and labelled the axes.

> **YES** – Go to question 3.
> **NO** – Go to 'Drawing and labelling axes'

3 I picked a sensible scale for each axis.

> **YES** – Go to question 4.
> **NO** – Go to 'Drawing axes and picking the scale'

4 I knew which variable to put on which axis.

> **YES** – Go to question 5.
> **NO** – Go to 'Which variable goes where?'

5 I got to this point and then got stuck.

> **YES** – Go to 'Drawing and labelling axes helper'
> **NO** – Go to question 6.

6 I plotted the data onto the graph with no problems.

> **YES** – Go to question 7.
> **NO** – Go to 'Plotting data on a line graph, part 1'

7 I think I could spot any mistakes made in plotting data on a line graph.

> **YES** – Go to question 8.
> **NO** – Go to 'Spot the mistakes'

8 I added a line or curve of best fit.

> **YES** – Go to question 9.
> **NO** – Go to 'Adding a line of best fit'

9 I gave the graph a descriptive title.

> **YES** – Go to question 10.
> **NO** – Go to 'And finally…'

10 I can draw a line graph successfully.

> **YES** – Go to 'Practice graph'
> Read 'Top Tips for success with line graphs'
> Try 'Marking a graph'.
> Try 'SAT-style question'
> Now go to question 11.

11 I can find and describe a pattern in a line graph.

> **YES** – Go to question 12.
> **NO** – 'Reading graphs – looking for a pattern – information'

Science Skills

12 I can read information from a line graph, such as finding a particular value.

YES – Go to question 13.
NO – 'Reading graphs for information'

13 I know how to extend (extrapolate) a line graph and when this can be useful.

YES – Go to question 14.
NO – Go to 'Extending a graph'

14 I can use a graph to work things out.

YES – Go to question 15.
NO – Go to 'Using a graph to work things out – parts 1 and 2'

15 I am confident with reading information from other types of graph, such as a bar chart and pie chart.

YES – Go to question 16.
NO – Go to 'Working with other types of graphs'

16 I am ready to draw a line graph and use it to answer questions.

YES – Go to 'Drawing and using a graph (final assessment)'

Drawing axes 1

Graphs can give you lots of information and really tell you the story of what is happening in a reaction or event. To plot a line graph you need to have two sets of numerical data – once this is plotted on a graph you can often see patterns more clearly, and the story told by the graph begins to reveal itself.

However, before you can do this the graph has to be set up and organised correctly – a bit like putting page numbers in a book and adding a contents list, so that you can find your way around easily.

The axes are the straight lines that start the graph. We add a scale to each axis and also a label so that we know what the numbers on the scale refer to.

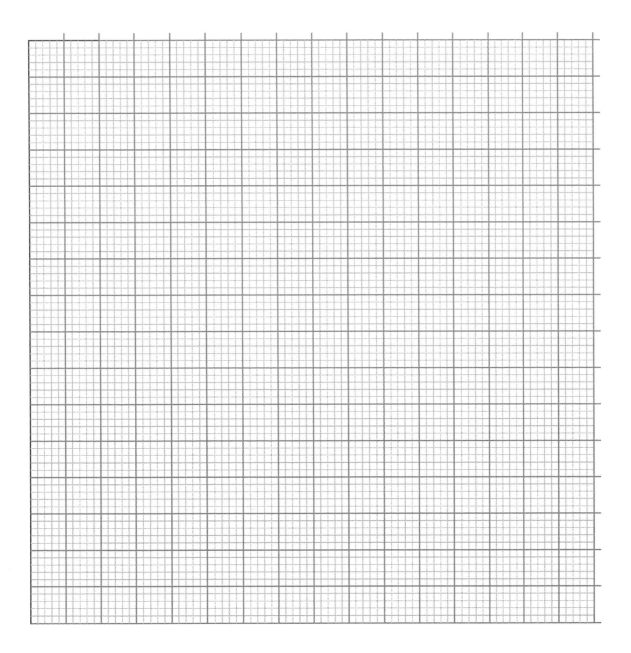

Use the information below to help you draw a set of axes and a scale on the graph paper. In this example the steps below will take you through the process.

Paul collected these results from an experiment:

Time (minutes)	Mass (g)
0	0
5	10
10	20
15	30
20	40
25	50
30	60

Step 1 – Building axes

Work out the minimum and maximum values for time in this experiment. This is important as they will be used as the bottom and top number on the horizontal axis (line along the bottom).

What is the range of numbers for the time?

Time has a range from 0 to 30 minutes.

It is best to start each line (or axis) with zero, so here the time axis will go from 0 to 30. You will also need to spread the numbers out so they are uniformly spaced. Don't draw the axis just yet!

TOP TIP

Most line graphs start each axis at 0. This is a useful rule to follow even if the data you want to plot starts at a higher number.

Step 2 – Building axes

Now that you have your range, you must decide on a scale you want to use.

What will each box on the time axis represent? It could represent 1 minute, 5 minutes, 10 minutes etc...

It makes most sense here to make each small square represent 1 minute.

Always make sure you can fit all your numbers on the page before you draw an axis.

Now, draw the horizontal axis on the graph paper. Add the scale. You don't need to put every number from 0 to 30 on the axis, you could just put every 5 and 10 minutes.

Step 3 – Building axes

Label the axis so you know what the numbers mean.

In this case the label should be 'Time (minutes)'.

TOP TIP

Make the scale large enough so that you can read off information easily, but not so large that it will not fit on the graph paper.

Step 4 – Building axes

Follow steps 1–3 and draw in a vertical axis (line going from the bottom to top) with a scale and label.

Drawing and labelling axes

Sometimes the numbers we want to use are not equally spaced out as a scale on the axis. An example of this is shown in the table.

Sabrina measured the temperature as she heated up some water in a beaker. Look at her table of results.

Time (minutes)	Temperature (°C)
0	0
1	21
2	32
3	43
4	55

Look at the values in the temperature column of the results table.

They are in order but there are obviously gaps between the numbers. If this was a book, and the numbers represented the pages you had to read, it would be very difficult to make any sense of the story at all – there's just too much information left out.

So, when you draw the axis for temperature you need to put in all the information, i.e. all the page numbers.

Follow these steps to help you and draw the axes on the small graph on the next page.

1 Work out the minimum and maximum values for temperature in this experiment. This is important as they will be used as the bottom and top number on the axis.

   What is the range of numbers for the temperature?

   Temperature has a range from 0 °C – 55 °C.

   It is best to start each line (or axis) with zero, so here the temperature axis will go from 0 to 55.

   If you wanted to you could make the axis go up to 60 °C. This will allow you to use your graph to predict information up to 60 °C and carry on the story.

TOP TIP

Most line graphs start each axis at 0. This is a useful rule to follow even if the data you want to plot starts at a higher number.

2 Now that you have your range, you must decide on a scale you want to use.

What will each box on the temperature axis represent?
It could represent 1 °C, 2 °C, 5 °C, 10 °C etc...

3 Complete the temperature axis on the graph below. Remember to keep the numbers evenly spaced.

TOP TIP

Make your scale large enough so that you can read off information easily, but not so large that it will not fit on the graph paper.

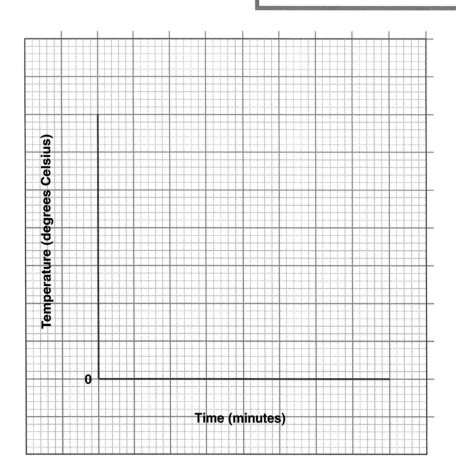

4 Plot the scale for the time axis.

Drawing and labelling axes – additional help sheet

Three pupils did the drawing and labelling axes task on page 5.4. Who did it correctly, Ann, Brett or Cheng? Put a tick in the box.

Ann ☐

Brett ☐

Cheng ☐

Why did you pick that set of axes?

Ann

_____

Brett

_____

Cheng

_____

5.5

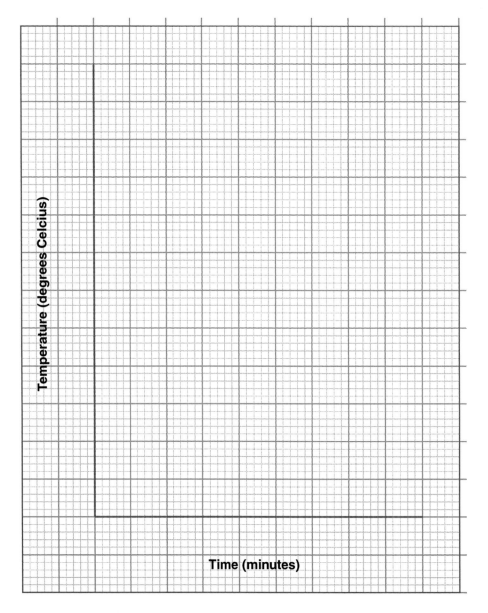

Drawing axes and picking the scale

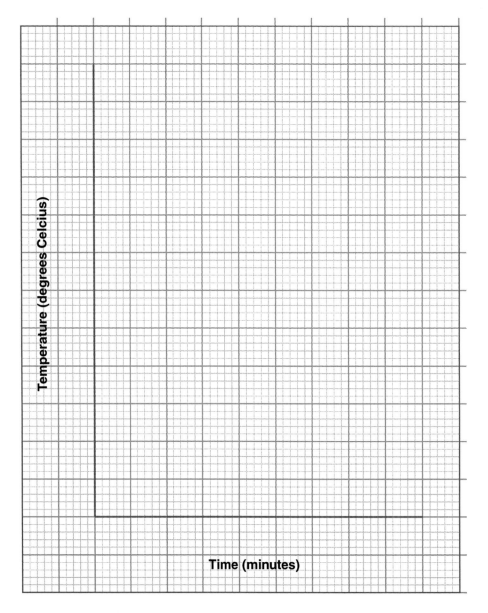

In an experiment Steve measured the temperature of 300 cm^3 iced water in a beaker until it boiled.

His results were:

Time (minutes)	Temperature (°C)
0	1
1	12
2	33
3	79
4	100
5	100

5.6   1/2

Science Skills

Choose and draw a simple scale for each axis. You can go back and look at the 'Drawing and labelling axes' worksheet to give you some tips.

For example:

1 The time axis scale could be 10 small squares for each minute, **or** it could be 5 small squares for each minute.

Which do you think is best?

Draw in the scale for your time axis now.

2 The temperature axis scale could be 10 small squares for each 10 °C, **or** it could be 5 small squares for each 10 °C.

Look carefully – which one will fit on the graph paper you have?

Could you use a better scale?

Draw in the scale for temperature now.

TOP TIP

Drawing axes and picking the scale is a skill that most pupils find hardest when drawing line graphs. If you are still not sure, please ask your teacher before moving on. Understanding this will help you do better and improve your grades.

Checklist
Before moving on, review your learning and understanding.

☐ I can draw a horizontal axis and a vertical axis to start a graph.

☐ I can pick a sensible scale for an axis.

☐ I can write the number scale onto the axis correctly.

☐ I can add a label on each axis to explain what the numbers mean.

Which variable goes where?

When you collect two sets of numerical data you can plot a line graph. You need to decide which variable will be represented on which axis so that the graph makes most sense.

For these experiments which variable will go on the horizontal axis? Fill in the gaps to answer the questions.

1   Manesh investigated how much heat was produced when he burnt 1.0 g of fuel. He placed the gram of fuel into a burner underneath a beaker containing 500 cm^3 of water. Once the fuel was alight Manesh measured the temperature change of the water until the fuel ran out.

   He continued his experiment seeing what happened when he used 1.5 g, 2.0 g, 2.5 g and 3.0 g fuel.

   When plotting a line graph of his results Manesh put _Which variable?_____ on the horizontal axis.

2   Stacey is investigating how the potential difference (voltage) across a resistance wire in a circuit increases when you increase the current.

   When plotting a line graph of her results Stacey put _Which variable?_____ on the horizontal axis.

3   Carl has been asked to find out how much alkali is needed to neutralise different concentrations of an acidic solution.

   When plotting a line graph of his results Carl put _Which variable?_____ on the horizontal axis.

4   A pupil was asked to prove the information written in a textbook that enzymes are affected by temperature. She set up an experiment using hydrogen peroxide. Hydrogen peroxide is broken down into oxygen and water when poured over a piece of raw liver. This is because the liver contains an enzyme that speeds up this reaction.

   The pupil measured how much gas was produced by the reaction at room temperature and then repeated the experiment in water baths set to different temperatures.

   When plotting a line graph of her results the pupil put _Which variable?_____ on the horizontal axis.

Drawing and labelling axes helper

The diagram below will remind you of the stages you need to follow when setting up a line graph. If you get stuck on further activities, or you are not sure where to start a graph, this is a good page to refer back to.

Setting up a line graph

Step 1 - Work out which variable will go on the horizontal axis - remember this will be the independent variable or the one that was controlled by the scientist

Step 2 - Work out the minimum and maximum values for the variable on the horizontal axis.

Step 3 - Work out what each square on the graph paper will represent.

Step 4 - Make sure you can fit your chosen scale on to the graph paper.

Draw in pencil

Use a ruler to draw straight axes

Step 5 - Draw the horizontal axis on your graph paper and plot your scale. Make sure the numbers are uniformly spaced.

Step 6 - Follow steps 2 – 5 to draw the vertical axis.

Step 7 - Label both axes with the variable and units.

Some graph paper has a thicker line surrounding a ten by ten box of small squares – this might help you when placing the axes.

Axes are best drawn so that they meet at the bottom left hand corner of the graph paper – leave some space so you can fit your labels.

The numbers in the scale need to be spread evenly so that the story told by the graph will make sense. If you don't do this it's a bit like missing out pages in a book – you simply can't make sense of the story.

The 0 should start at the point where the two axes cross.

5.8

Plotting data on a line graph – part 1

Now we have set up the axes we need to add some information to give us a story to read.

Spend some time working out what each square on the graph represents. For example, on the graph used on this page, each small square on the temperature axis equals 0.5 °C.

You need to know this so that you can plot data. Plotting data (putting points onto a graph) is a bit like reading a map.

Let's use the second set of points (highlighted in the table below) as an example of how to plot a point on a graph.

- First, find 1 minute on the time axis – draw a pencil line directly up from this point.
- Next, find 5 °C on the temperature axis – draw a pencil line directly out (horizontal) from this point.
- Mark an 'x' where the two lines cross to plot the point. This is very similar to the way you would read coordinates on a map to find a location.
- Now plot the rest of the points using the same technique.

Time (minutes)	Temperature (°C)
0	0
1	5
2	7
3	15
4	21
5	30

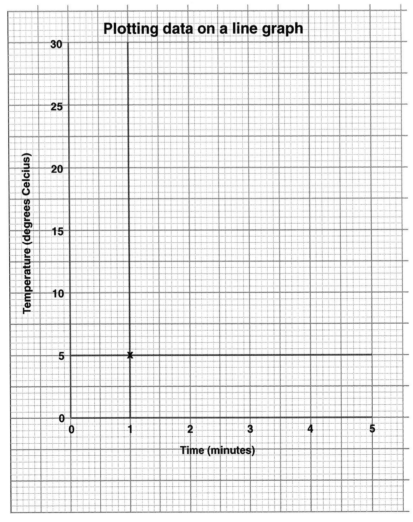

5.9

Plotting data on a line graph – part 2

Plotting data is a good skill to practice and one you need to be able to do to produce line graphs. Here's another chance to have a go – if you are really not sure please ask your teacher for more help.

Nicole's experiment

Nicole wanted to find out how much vitamin C was in different concentrations of her favourite fruit juice. She measured out 2 cm^3 of a blue chemical called DCPIP and put it into a test tube. DCPIP loses its colour when it is mixed with vitamin C. Nicole added drops of the fruit juice until the DCPIP lost its colour.

Concentration of fruit juice (%)	Number of fruit juice drops needed to turn DCPIP clear
100	2
75	8
50	16
25	32

The table shows her results. Plot the data from the table onto the graph using the skills you have developed so far.

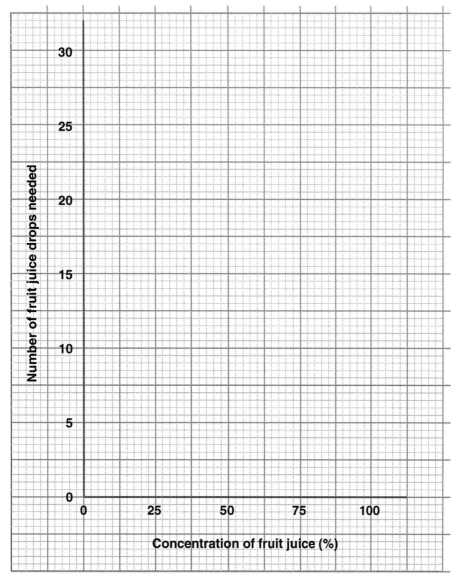

Plotting data on a line graph – part 2

Plotting data is a good skill to practice and one you need to be able to do to produce line graphs. Here's another chance to have a go – if you are really not sure please ask your teacher for more help.

Nicole's experiment

Nicole wanted to find out how much vitamin C was in different concentrations of her favourite fruit juice. She measured out 2 cm^3 of a blue chemical called DCPIP and put it into a test tube. DCPIP loses its colour when it is mixed with vitamin C. Nicole added drops of the fruit juice until the DCPIP lost its colour.

Concentration of fruit juice (%)	Number of fruit juice drops needed to turn DCPIP clear
100	2
75	8
50	16
25	32

The table shows her results. Draw some appropriate axes and plot the data from the table onto the graph using the skills you have developed so far.

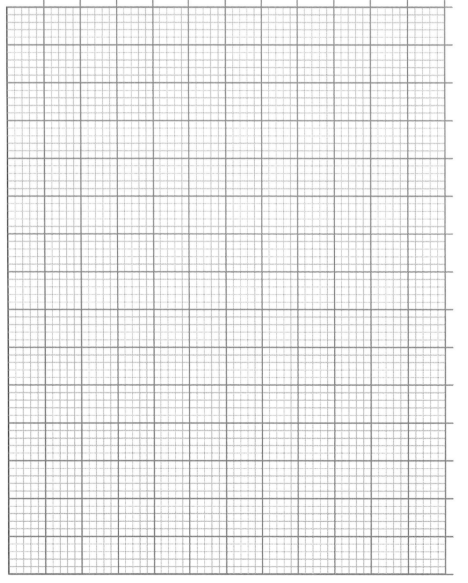

TOP TIP

If you get stuck on this see if any of the previous exercises in your Skills File can help you.

Make sure you can do this before moving on. If you can't, stop and ask.

5.10h

Spot the mistakes

You've had lots of practice now in setting up a graph. Some others pupils have also tried it but have made a few errors! Use your detective skills to spot the mistakes on the graphs below – ring them with a coloured pen. Some of the mistakes might be things that have been left out.

Graph 1

Find at least three mistakes.

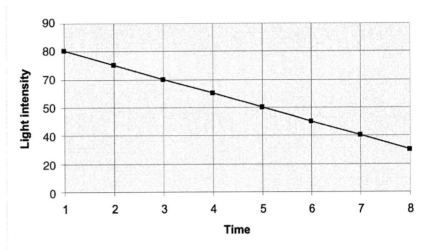

Graph 2

Find at least three mistakes.

Amount of fuel used	Cost (£)
1	2.0
2	4.0
3	6.0
4	8.0
5	10.0
6	9.9
7	13.0
8	14.5
9	15.0
10	17.5

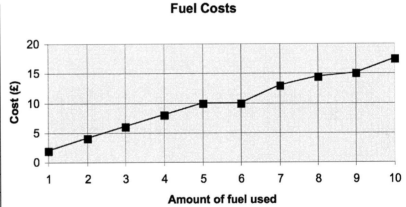

Graph 3

How many mistakes can you find?

Size of Animal	Food Consumed
1	2
3	9
5	25
6	36
9	81
8	64
4	8
2	4
10	100
12	120
15	180

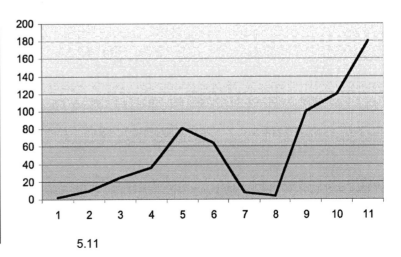

5.11

Adding a line of best fit

A line or curve of best fit is drawn so that the points are evenly distributed on either side of the line. Sometimes the line joins the points together, sometimes it doesn't!

Here are some examples.

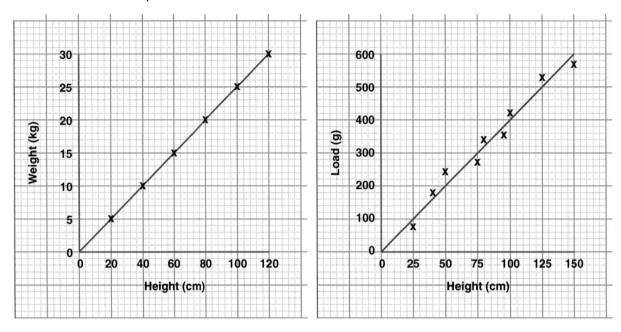

This is done so a pattern can be seen more easily and the story of the graph becomes clearer.

In each set of graphs below, pick the line of best fit and tick the box.

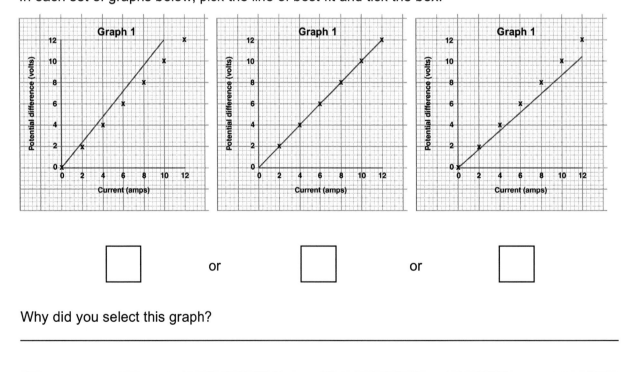

☐   or   ☐   or   ☐

Why did you select this graph?

_____

_____

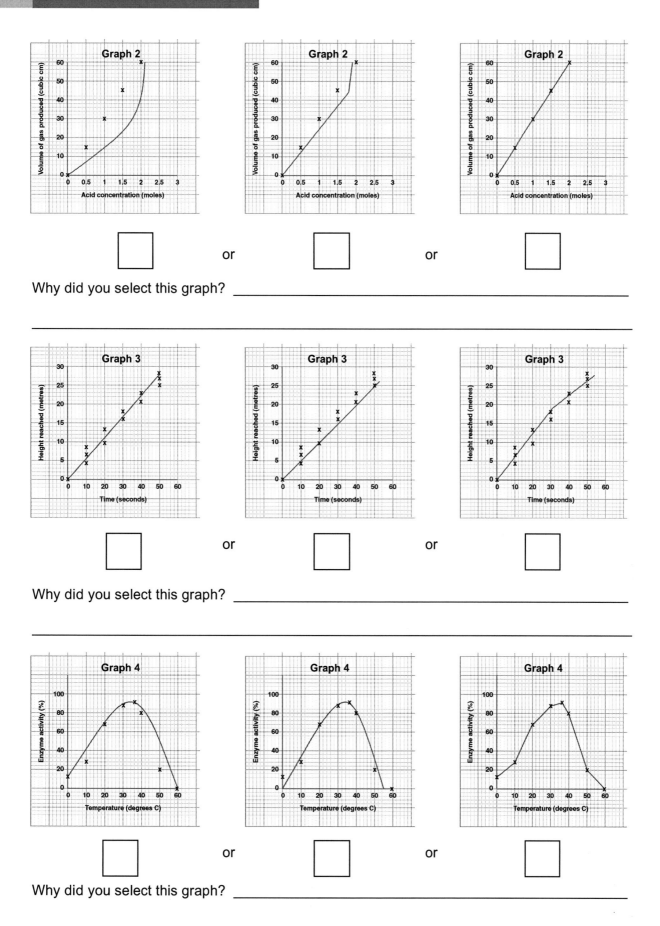

Why did you select this graph? _____

Why did you select this graph? _____

Why did you select this graph? _____

5.12e   2/2

Adding a line of best fit

A line or curve of best fit is drawn so that the points are evenly distributed on either side of the line. Sometimes the line joins the points together, sometimes it doesn't!

Here are some examples.

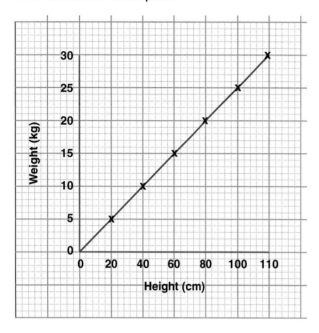

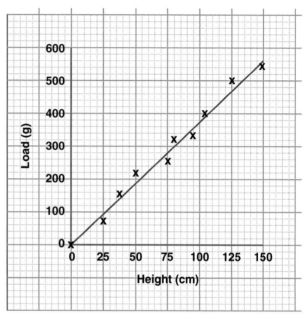

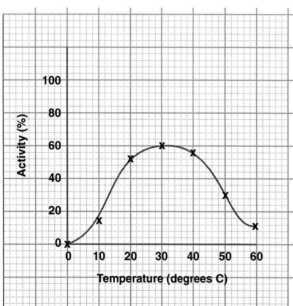

This is done so a pattern can be seen more easily and the story of the graph becomes clearer.

Add the line or curve of best fit to the other four graphs in this section. The first one is below.

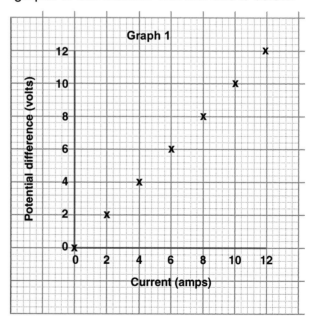

5.12h   1/2

Science Skills

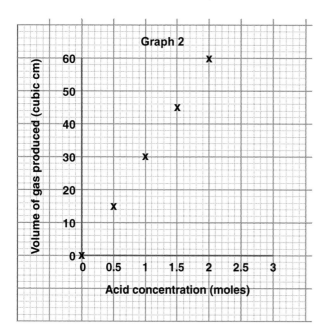

TOP TIP

You don't have to draw your line or curve of best fit through '0, 0'

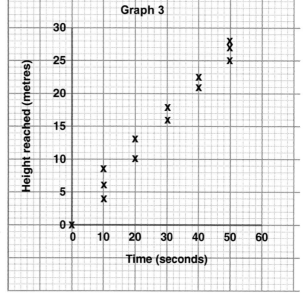

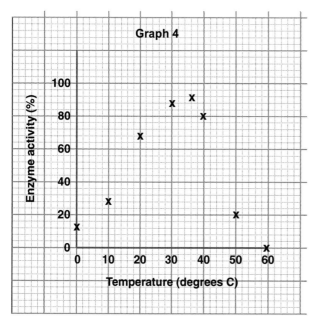

And finally… (writing the title for a graph)

Give your graph a title that describes it. After all every story needs a good title.

A graph should have a descriptive title such as: 'A graph to show the effect of temperature on enzyme activity'. The clues come from the axis labels.

Suggest some titles for these graphs:

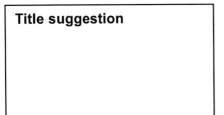

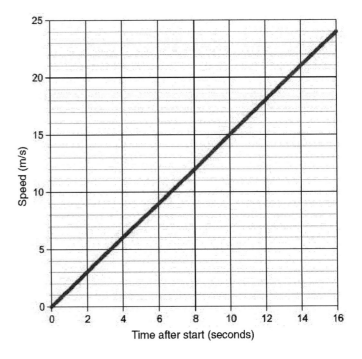

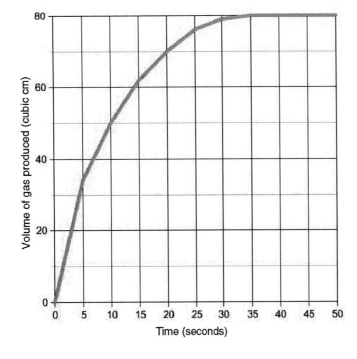

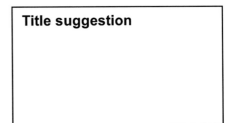

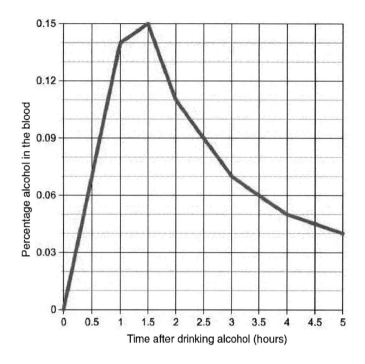

Title suggestion

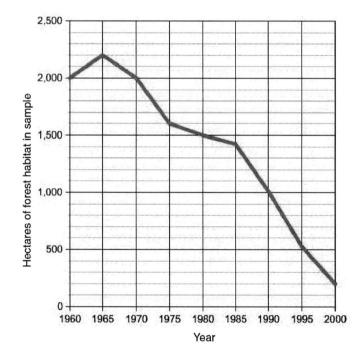

Title suggestion

TOP TIP

The more descriptive the axis labels, the more descriptive your title can be.

5.13   2/2

Practice graph

Let's put all these skills to use.

Plot this data. (Use notes in your Skills File to help you.)

Time (hours)	Distance travelled (km)
0	0
2	10
4	30
6	50
8	80
10	100
12	140

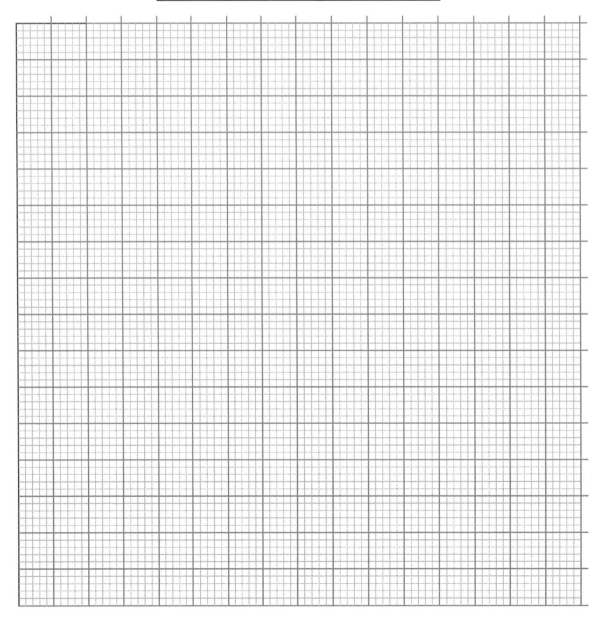

5.14

Checklist

The graph has a title.

☐ The axes are drawn as straight lines. I used a ruler to do this.

☐ Both axes are labelled with the variable and the units.

☐ The scale used is sensible and the numbers are placed at uniform intervals.

☐ All the points have been marked clearly and accurately.

☐ There is a line or curve of best fit.

The checklist above is for you to use before you hand in your graph for marking.

It also shows you what your teacher is looking for and how you can get the best mark for your work.

Science Skills

Top tips for success with line graphs

✔ Draw and label graphs in pencil on graph paper.

✔ Add a title.

✔ Put the variable you control (the independent variable) on the horizontal axis (bottom line).

✔ Look at the maximum value you need to include for each axis. Make sure you have enough room on each axis to fit this range.

✔ Explain, to yourself, what each box on your graph represents,
   i.e. 1 unit, 5 units, 10 units.

✔ Make sure the numbers in the scale are uniformly spaced.

✔ Label each axis – remember to include units.

   For example:
   • mass (grams)
   • time (minutes)
   • weight (newtons)

✔ Plot points accurately and neatly so they are easy to see. A cross is probably the best way to do this but you will see graphs that use dots, diamonds and other simple symbols to mark the point.

✔ Draw a neat line or curve of best fit in pencil.

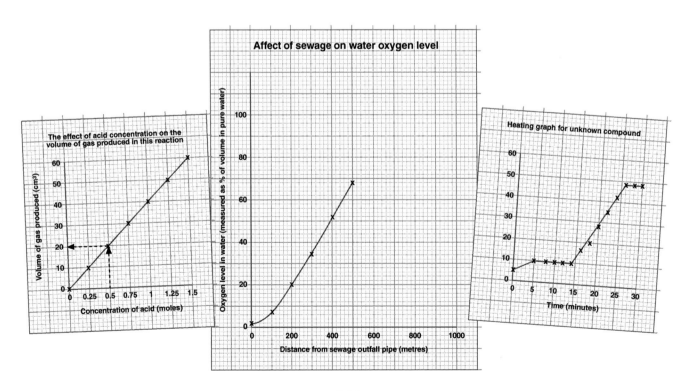

5.16

Marking a graph

You now know how to draw a graph and plot data on it. You even know what your teacher will be looking for when they mark a graph, but here's your chance to have a go.

Read the information and look at the graph. Mark the pupil's work using the marking grid on the next page. In the final column write one or two sentences of feedback telling the pupil how to improve.

The experiment

Lucy carried out an ecological survey on a piece of salt marsh on an estuary. She measured the species cover of a plant called samphire in a 1 m^2 quadrant. She started at the low tide mark and took measurements at 20-metre intervals.

Here are her results.

Distance from low tide mark (metres)	% cover of samphire in 1 m^2
0	0
20	10
40	15
60	30
80	70
100	100
120	100
140	60
160	20
180	5
200	0
220	0

Here is the graph Lucy plotted using this data.

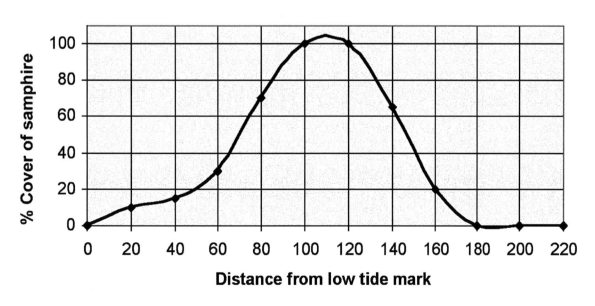

Samphire Cover on Saltmarsh

5.17   1/2

Graph marking grid

How good is Lucy's graph? Record your marks here and remember to give constructive feedback.

Question	Maximum marks you can award	Marks awarded	Feedback comment
Does the graph have a title that tells you something about the graph?	1		
Is the independent variable on the horizontal axis?	1		
Is the horizontal axis labelled?	1 mark for variable 1 mark for units		
Are the points on the horizontal axis spread uniformly and plotted correctly?	2		
Is the vertical axis labelled?	1 mark for variable 1 mark for units		
Are the points on the vertical axis spread uniformly and plotted correctly?	2		
Are the axes scales sensible so that you can read the numbers?	1 mark for each axis		
Are the points plotted correctly?	1 mark for each point plotted correctly		
Has a sensible symbol been used for each point?	1		
Is there a line or curve of best fit?	1		
Is the line or curve of best fit a good match for the data?	1		
Are there any problems with the line or curve of best fit?	1		
TOTAL			

SAT-style question

Five groups of pupils carried out an experiment, burning different masses of peanut to heat 20 cm^3 of water for 1 minute. In each case the starting temperature of the water was 22 °C.

Their results are shown in the table:

	A	B	C	D	E
Mass of peanut (g)	0.9	1.2	1.5	1.8	2.1
End temperature of water (°C)	32.0	39.0	48.0	42.0	67.0
Temperature rise (°C)	10.0				

1   Finish the table by working out the temperature change of the water in each experiment. One has been done for you. (2 marks)

2   On the grid plot the results of each group. Draw a line of best fit. (6 marks)

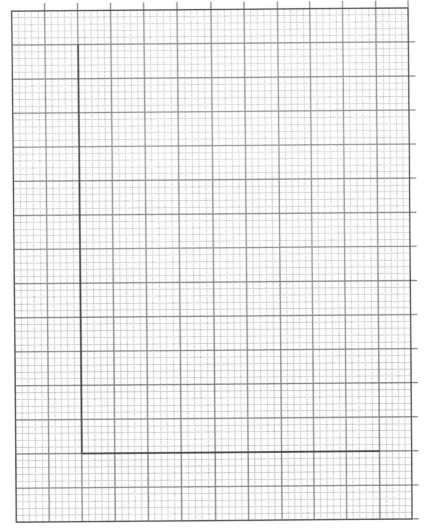

3   From the graph, why do you think that the results of group D are not correct? (1 mark)

_____

Reading graphs – looking for a pattern – information

Once created, a graph has a story to tell.

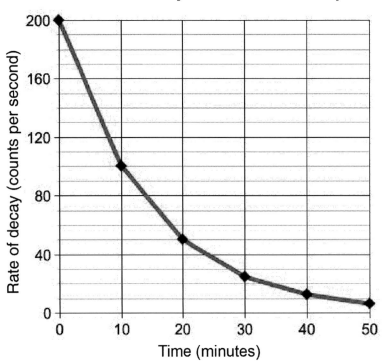

Radioactive decay of an unknown compound

What's the story?

Things to look for in a graph.

1 Is there a pattern?
   Look at the independent variable – the one the scientist decided on, in this case 'time' as she decided on the time intervals. As time increases, what happens to the other variable?

   → As time increases, the rate decreases.

2 Is this pattern constant?

   → As time increases, the rate decreases quickly at first and then more slowly. The rate of decrease drops by half every ten minutes.

3 What's the story behind the story?
   Can you use your scientific knowledge to suggest why this is?

   → Radioactive materials are not stable and decay. The time taken for the radioactive decay to decrease by half is called the half-life. The half-life of the unknown compound is 10 minutes.

5.19

Reading graphs – looking for a pattern – easier

Look for the pattern in these examples:

Example 1

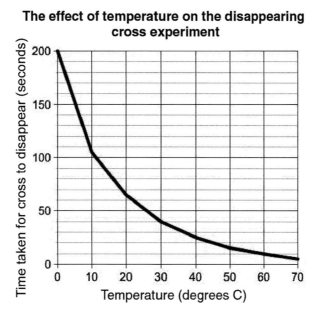

The effect of temperature on the disappearing cross experiment

What is the pattern? Cross out the wrong words.

As the temperature **increases / decreases** the time taken for the cross to disappear **increases / decreases**. The cross disappears quickest at the **highest / lowest** temperature.

Example 2

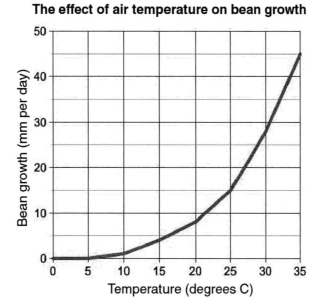

The effect of air temperature on bean growth

What is the pattern? Cross out the wrong words.

As the temperature **increases / decreases** the bean grows **more / less** each day. The bean starts growing when the air temperature is **5 / 8 / 12 °C**.

5.20e

Reading graphs – looking for a pattern – harder

Example 3

The effect of temperature on the rate of reaction

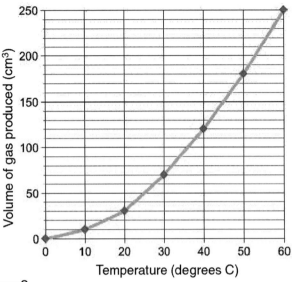

What is the pattern?

→ As the temperature _____

Example 4

Petrol consumption at different speeds for a kit car

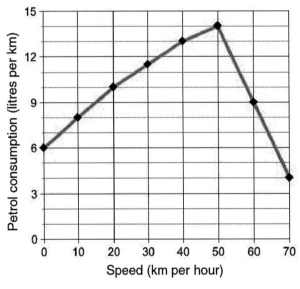

TOP TIP

In a graph where there are two or more patterns, describe both patterns. The example left has been started for you.

What is the pattern?

→ Between a speed of 0 km/h and 50 km/h, as the speed _____

_____

Between 50 km/h and 70 km/h _____

_____

Example 5

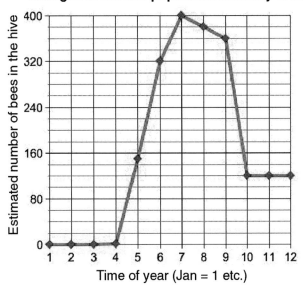

Changes in the bee population at honey hive

What is the pattern? Describe each stage of the graph.

_____

_____

_____

_____

_____

_____

_____

_____

Reading graphs for information

Sometimes you need to read a graph to find out one particular fact; it's just like using the index in a book to find the right page.

The graph below shows you how to do this.

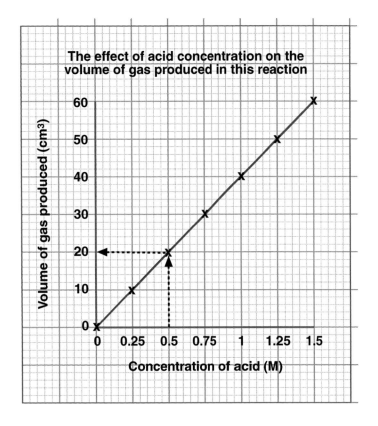

The effect of acid concentration on the volume of gas produced in this reaction

1 How much gas is produced when the acid concentration is 0.5 M?

To do this:
- Read along the 'Concentration of acid' axis until you find 0.5 M.
- Draw an imaginary straight line, or pencil line, directly up from 0.5 M until you hit the line of best fit.
- To find the volume of gas, draw another straight line horizontally from the point on the line of best fit until it crosses the 'Volume of gas produced' axis.
- Read the number off the axis – this is the volume produced, in this case 20 cm^3.

Try these questions using the same technique on the graph above.

2 What volume of gas is produced by 1 M acid?
   a   10 cm^3
   b   20 cm^3
   c   30 cm^3
   d   40 cm^3

3 What volume of gas is produced by 0.75 M acid?
   a   10 cm^3
   b   20 cm^3
   c   30 cm^3
   d   40 cm^3

4. What concentration of acid is needed to produce 50 cm^3 of gas?
   a   0.75 M
   b   1.00 M
   c   1.25 M
   d   1.50 M

Reading graphs for information

Answer these questions by reading information from the graph below.

1 What temperature does the compound reach after ten minutes of heating?

_____

2 What temperature does the compound reach after 25 minutes of heating?

_____

3 How long does it take for the compound to reach 20 °C? _____

4 How long does the compound stay at 10 °C? _____

5 How long did it take for the compound to be heated to 48 °C? _____

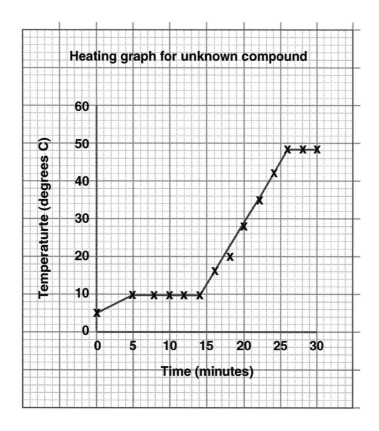

5.21h

Extending a graph

You can extend a graph beyond the plotted points to help you predict what might happen next beyond the scope of the measured points. It's a bit like writing your own next chapter in a book after you have learnt all about the characters and the story.

This process is called **extrapolation**. It is most reliable with graphs that show a straightforward pattern.

In the graph below the scientist measured the gas produced between 0 °C and 30 °C. What volume of gas is produced at 40 °C?

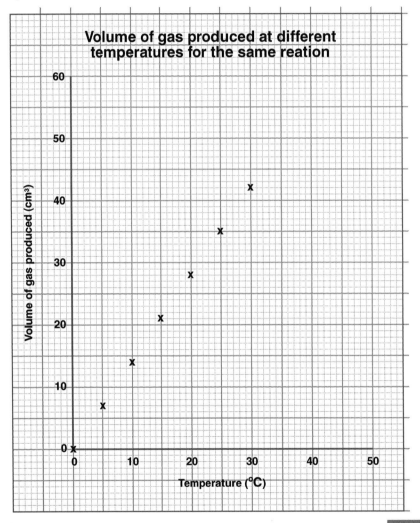

To work this out.

1   Draw in a line or curve of best fit.

2   To extrapolate, continue the line or curve of best fit beyond the last measured point.

3   Read the information off the graph, just as you have done before.

At 40 °C, the volume of gas produced is _____ cm^3.

Beware – this method assumes that the pattern shown on the graph, up to the points that were measured, will continue. This is not always the case!

5.22

Using a graph to work things out – part 1

Now we are going to start putting together all the skills you have covered so far by using graphs to help us find out lots of information.

Remember, if you get stuck you now have your own Skills File of information to look back on. That's not cheating – it's being smart!

Answer the questions using information from the graph.

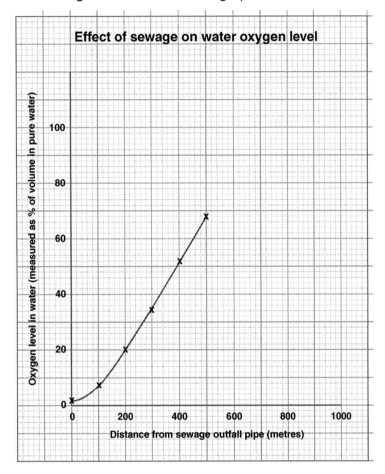

1   What is the oxygen level 100 metres along the river from the sewage outfall pipe?

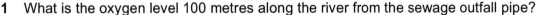

| 8% | 50% | 70% | 100% |

2   What is the oxygen level 600 metres along the river?

| 55% | 67% | 84% | 98% |

(You need to extend the line of best fit to find this out.)

3   What is the oxygen level 350 metres along the river?

| 34% | 46% | 58% | 70% |

4 What happens to the oxygen level in the water as you go further downstream beyond the outfall pipe?

| It decreases | It stays the same | It increases |

5 A dragonfly larva needs a 60% oxygen level to survive. What is the first point past the sewage outfall pipe that this insect might be found?

| 240 m | 350 m | 460 m | 570m |

6 At what distance from the outfall pipe will the water return to the 100% oxygen level?

| 400 m | 500 m | 600 m | 700 m |

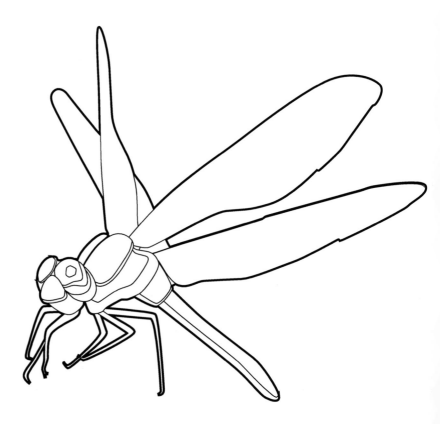

Using a graph to work things out – part 1

Now we are going to start putting together all the skills you have covered so far by using graphs to help us find out lots of information.

Remember, if you get stuck you now have your own Skills File of information to look back on. That's not cheating – it's being smart!

Add a line or curve of best fit to the graph below.

Answer the questions using information from the graph.

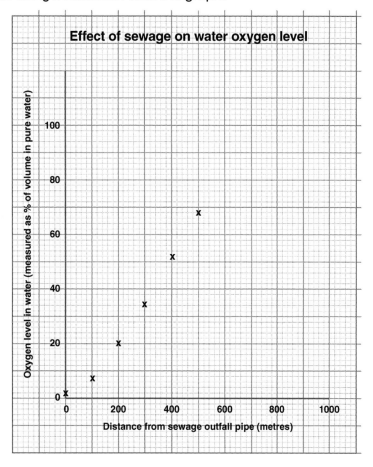

1   What is the oxygen level 100 metres along the river from the sewage outfall pipe?
_____

2   What is the oxygen level 600 metres along the river? _____ (You need to extend the line of best fit to find this out.)

3   What is the oxygen level 350 metres along the river? _____

4   What happens to the oxygen level in the water as you go further downstream beyond the outfall pipe?

_____

_____

5.23h   1/2

5   A dragonfly larva needs a 60% oxygen level to survive. What is the first point past the sewage outfall pipe that this insect might be found? _____ metres

6   At what distance from the outfall pipe will the water return to the 100% oxygen level? _____ metres

7   Will the oxygen level in the water continue to increase passed this point? Think carefully about this – what is the real story of the graph? How far can it be extended?

_____

_____

Using a graph to work things out – part 2

Some graphs might look complicated to begin with but they are still telling you a story. Just as before, read along the horizontal axis, in this case 'time', and ask yourself 'what story am I being told at each point in time?'

You might look at this graph and start to build the following story.

- At 0 to 1 minute the rider was increasing her speed.

- Between 1 to 2 minutes into the journey the speed is still increasing but much more slowly so that at 2 minutes the rider's speed is _____ metres per second.

- After 2 minutes the bicycle rider slows down until she stops altogether at _____ minutes into the journey.

- From 4 minutes the journey of the bicycle suddenly _____.

- I know this because the speed increased to _____ metres per second at 5 minutes.

Fill in the missing words and carry on to complete the story of the journey.

_____

_____

_____

_____

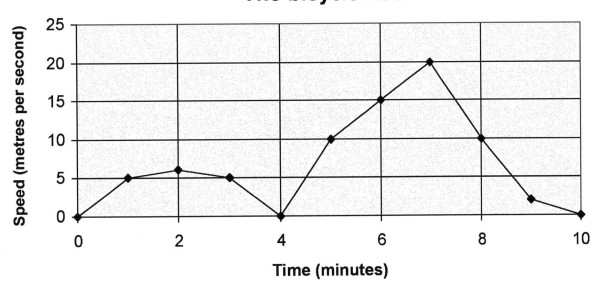

The bicycle ride

5.24   1/2

Use information from the graph to help you to answer these questions.

1 How long does it take the bicycle to reach a speed of 10 metres per second for the first time?

_____

2 How far does the bicycle travel in the first minute? _____

3 What kind of terrain might the cyclist be travelling over between minutes 4 and 7 of the journey?

_____

4 What is the bicycle doing between minutes 7 and 10 of the journey?

_____

Line of best fit

The story of the graph tells you about the journey of a bicycle. Why, in this case, do you think it is right to draw a line of best fit that joins the points together?

_____

_____

_____

Working with other types of graph

You might also need to read the story told by other types of graph. Try this out on the graphs in this section.

Best selling trainers

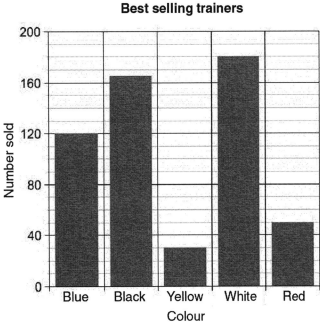

Best selling trainers

1 Which colour of trainer was most popular?

    a Blue   **b** Black   **c** Yellow   **d** White

2 Which colour was least popular?

    a Blue   **b** Red   **c** Yellow   **d** Black

3 How many red trainers were sold?

    a 30   **b** 40   **c** 50   **d** 60

4 Which trainer sold more, black or white?

    a Black   **b** White

Household pets

The results of a survey of household pets are shown in the graph. Each person surveyed owned only one kind of pet.

5 What percentage of people owned fish?

    a 1%   **b** 10%

    c 20%   **d** 50%

6 Of the groups shown, which is the largest?

    a Rabbit   **b** Cat

    c Fish   **d** Dog

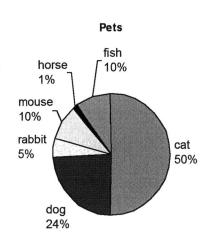

Pets

5.25e   1/2

Percentage of people owning different pets.

7 What percentage of people owned rabbits or dogs?

    a 11%   **b** 23%   **c** 29%   **d** 74%

8 Which two pets both claim 10% of the pie-chart?

    a Mice and fish **b** Horses and cats **c** Mice and cats   **d** Fish and rabbits

Number of visitors to London attractions

Number of visitors to London attractions

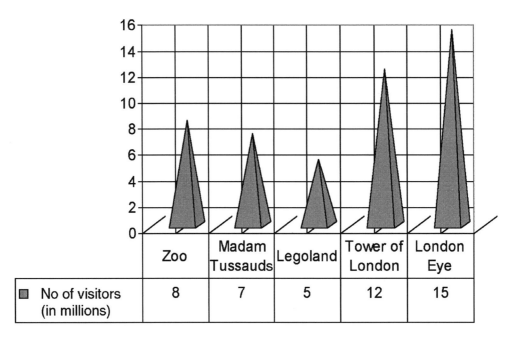

	Zoo	Madam Tussauds	Legoland	Tower of London	London Eye
▨ No of visitors (in millions)	8	7	5	12	15

9 What is the most visited attraction?

    a Tower of London   **b** London Eye   **c** Legoland **d** Zoo

10 How many people visited Legoland?

    a 8 million   **b** 10 million   **c** 5 million **d** 15 million

11 Which attraction was more popular, the Zoo or Madam Tussauds?

    a Zoo   **b** Madam Tussauds

12 Which attraction did 12 million people visit?

    a London Eye   **b** Tower of London **c** Zoo   **d** Legoland

Working with other types of graph

You might also need to read the story told by other types of graph. Try this out on the graphs in this section.

Best selling trainers

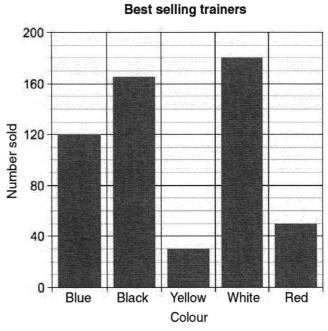

Best selling trainers

1   Which colour of trainer was most popular? _____

2   Which colour was least popular? _____

3   How many red trainers were sold? _____

4   Which trainer sold more, black or white? _____

Household pets

The results of a survey of household pets are shown in the graph.
Each person surveyed owned only one kind of pet.

5   What percentage of people owned fish?

_____

6   Of the groups shown, which is the largest?

_____

7   What percentage of people owned rabbits or dogs?

_____

8   Which two pets both claim 10% of the pie chart?

_____

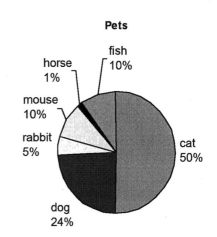

Pets

5.25h   1/2

Number of visitors to London attractions

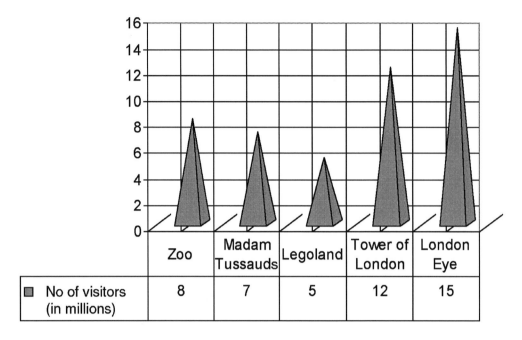

Number of visitors to London attractions

	Zoo	Madam Tussauds	Legoland	Tower of London	London Eye
▨ No of visitors (in millions)	8	7	5	12	15

9 What is the most visited attraction? _____

10 How many people visited Legoland? _____

11 Which attraction was more popular, the Zoo or Madam Tussauds?

_____

12 Which attraction did 12 million people visit? _____

Drawing and using a graph (final assessment)

Plot a line graph using the information given in the table and use it to answer the questions.

Living at high altitude poses problems for humans. At altitude the air is thinner and contains less oxygen than at lower altitudes.

Note: You will need to extrapolate your graph to read data at 4500 metres.

Altitude (metres above sea level)	Average number of red blood cells per cubic mm of blood (millions)
0	5.0
1500	5.5
3000	6.1
3600	6.5
4000	8.0

Questions

1 At what altitude is the average number of red blood cells per cubic mm of blood equal to 7 million?

_____

2 How many red blood cells per cubic mm of blood would be estimated in a person living at 2000 metres above sea level?

_____

3 Predict the number of red blood cells per cubic mm of blood for a person at 4500 metres above sea level.

_____

4 What pattern can be seen between altitude and the number of red blood cells per cubic mm of blood?

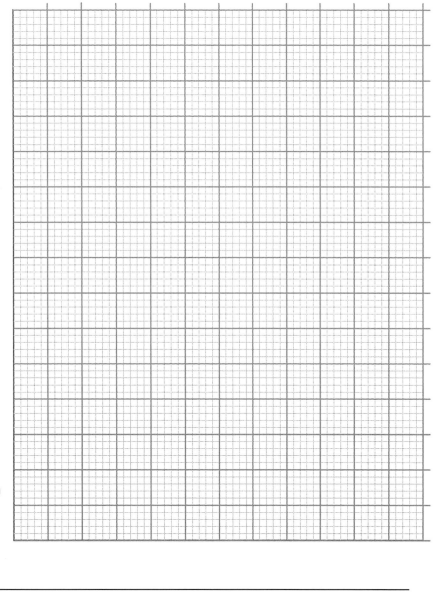

_____

_____

5.26

Final checklist

Well done!

You have completed at lot of work on graphs – I hope you now feel really confident about drawing and using line graphs.

You should be able to check off all the items on the list below.

- ☐ I can give a graph a descriptive title.
- ☐ I can draw the axes as straight lines. I use a ruler to do this.
- ☐ I can label both axes with the variable and the units.
- ☐ I know which variable should go on which axis.
- ☐ I can use a sensible scale for each axis and place the numbers at uniform intervals.
- ☐ I can plot all the points clearly and accurately.
- ☐ I can add a line or curve of best fit.
- ☐ I know how to read information from a graph.
- ☐ I can describe the pattern shown by the line or curve of best fit on a graph.
- ☐ I can extend the graph to find out further information (extrapolation).

TOP TIP

Remember you now have a great source of information to help you further. Keep it somewhere safe!

Practical work – planning, carrying out and reporting experiments

Teacher introduction

This section of the book aims to develop the skills needed to complete and understand the nature of practical work. Each area of reporting is dealt with in small chunks with worksheets and activities being ideal to use as starters or plenaries. The hope and expectation is that each pupil will build a resource that they find useful and refer back to when they undertake their Science Course at 14 – 16.

The content assumes that pupils are already familiar with and have some experience of carrying out scientific investigations. However, it does not assume that they are confident or well informed; basic points are recapped, and tasks are developed to help reinforce knowledge and self-confidence. The overall aim is to help pupils develop good practice. There is a formative self-assessment exercise that will help pupils to determine their own starting place in this section. However, the assessment may be best achieved by you working through it with them – this gives the opportunity to highlight the positives as well as the things that need to be worked on. To complete the self-assessment pupils need to refer to the last full piece of practical work they undertook.

When using the formative self-assessment pupils can either start from the point where they answered 'no' to the statement and work through the rest of the section, or complete that worksheet and then refer back to the self-assessment again. There is no formal end assessment to this section as it makes more sense that this should fall to the teacher who can select an investigation that fits into the current learning topic. However, there is a 'Practical work checklist' showing pupils the type of criteria their work is marked against.

The overall aim is to help pupils develop their thinking, sequencing and learning of the scientific process. I believe that if these skills can be mastered then the pupils gain confidence in what they are doing and in turn develop a much better and truer understanding of practical work. It also helps pupils to develop independent learning and encourages them to ask more questions about the topics they are studying – in short it engenders success.

This includes being healthy and safe and understanding health and safety – you may want to refer back to the Science lab health and safety rules (1.3) and consult the suggested health and safety resources listed at the front of the book. Advice on health and safety in the school laboratory is readily available, see

- CLEAPSS – advisory service supporting science and technology in schools and colleges throughout the United Kingdom (for Scotland see below). http://www.cleapss.org.uk/
- SSERC – advisory service supporting science and technology in schools and colleges in Scotland. http://www.sserc.org.uk/public/
- *Safeguards in the School Laboratory* (11th edition) published by ASE (ISBN 9780863574085)
- *Topics in Safety* (3rd edition) published by the ASE (ISBN 9780863573163)

Science Skills

Throughout I have tried to reinforce the need for accuracy and detail. I have suggested that a plan for any scientific experiment should be clear enough that another pupil is able to carry out the same experiment and get exactly the same results, within limitations – that an experiment is invalid if results cannot be replicated!

Results worksheets tackle reading measurements and recording data clearly, as well as asking pupils to recall and use their graph skills. Conclusions are dealt with by giving pupils plenty of opportunities to practice data analysis before moving on to consider evaluations. In my experience pupils find evaluations troublesome – hopefully the worksheets here will help to demystify the process and give them a chance to practice and receive feedback.

Throughout I hope you will encourage your pupils to question and develop an understanding as to why reports are written to such guidelines. A lot of the tasks have worked best for me followed by a short discussion and getting pupils to peer evaluate what they have been doing – despite my initial concerns most pupils really started to get to grips with the process and reasons through this method and frequently offered direct but constructive criticism on other pupils' work.

Introduction for pupils

When you do a piece of practical work in science you need to record information. There are worksheets that take you through each step of practical work. For some practical activities you may only be asked to report on some sections for the work you do in class.

The first thing to be sure of is the aim of the experiment. What are you trying to find out? Is there a question you are trying to answer? Once you have worked this out you can plan an experiment to answer the question.

The overview worksheet introduces planning an experiment and writing about your experiment.

The practical report writing frame will help you to organise your ideas for the next piece of practical work you do. There's not much space on a template like this but it might help you to remember each section and jot down some initial ideas before completing a proper scientific report.

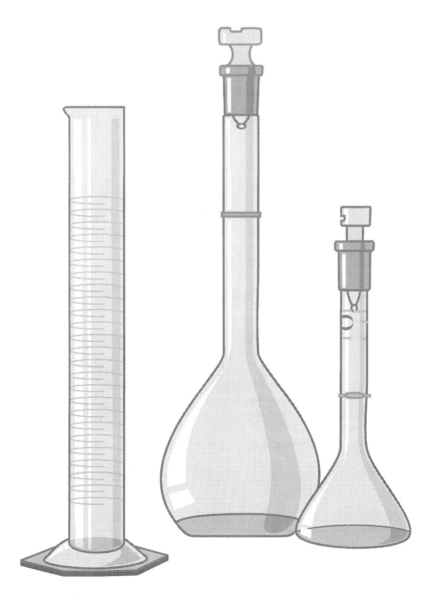

6.3

Practical report writing frame

The **AIM** of this experiment is

METHOD

APPARATUS

DIAGRAM

PREDICTION

RESULTS / OBSERVATIONS (Complete your graph on graph paper)

CONCLUSION

EVALUATION

6.4

Planning and writing about an experiment

Overview

When you carry out an investigation or experiment in science it is really useful to be able to tell another person about what you have found out. In science we do this by writing practical reports using subheadings.

PREDICT

What am I trying to find out? This is sometimes called the **aim**.
What do I think will happen, and why?

↓

PLAN = Research, Procedure, Apparatus, Diagram

How will I carry out my experiment?

- Fair test?
- What will I change?
- What will I keep the same?
- What will I measure?
- Is it healthy and safe?

↓

OBSERVE AND MEASURE (Results)

Which pieces of apparatus do I need?
How many times do I need to take the measurement?

↓

WORK OUT AND CONCLUDE

How will I show my findings?

- Table
- Graph
- Tally chart

Is there any pattern in my results?
Can I use science to explain what I have found out?

↓

EVALUATE

Are my results accurate?
Can I rely on the results?
How could I make this experiment better and even more accurate?
What experiment could I do next to continue to prove this idea?

6.5

Practical work – self-assessment

You are now going to assess the last piece of practical work you did to find out which worksheet you need to do next.

You need to be honest and answer YES or NO to each statement.

1   I wrote an aim for the experiment.   **YES** – Go to question 2.
                                                                NO – Go to 'What is the aim?'

2   I wrote a clear method with lots of detail.   **YES** – Go to question 3.
     I think another pupil could follow   **NO** – Go to 'Planning – method'
     this method.

3   I repeated my experimental measurements   **YES** – Go to question 4.
     more than once to make sure my results   **NO** – Go to 'One more time!'
     were consistent.

4   My experiment was a fair test.   **YES** – Go to question 5.
                                                   NO – Go to 'Fair tests'

5   I can pick the right piece of equipment to   **YES** – Go to question 6.
     make the most accurate measurements.   **NO** – Go to 'Measuring accurately'

6   I know how to draw apparatus.   **YES** – Go to question 7.
     I included a diagram in my experiment.   **NO** – Go to 'Drawing apparatus'

7   I included a prediction.   **YES** – Go to question 8
     The prediction included a reason.   **NO** – Go to 'Predicting'

8   I can write a good plan including health   **YES** – Go to 'It seems like a good plan'
     and safety issues, taking account of   **NO** – Go to 'Planning practice'
     hazards and adopting suitable precautions.

9   I can find out the volume of a liquid.   **YES** – Go to question 10.
                                                   NO – Go to 'Reading measurements –
                                                   liquid volume'

10   I can find read information from   **YES** – Go to question 11.
     a thermometer.   **NO** – Go to 'Reading measurements –
                                                   temperature'

11   I can make accurate measurements   **YES** – Go to question 12.
     of length.   **NO** – Go to 'Reading measurements –
                                                   length'

12 I can use a newton meter to take force readings.

YES – Go to question 13.
NO – Go to 'Reading measurements – force'

13 I can present results in a clear way.

YES – Go to question 14.
NO – Go to 'What is the best way to present my results?'

14 I can give a table a title to describe it.

YES – Go to question 15.
NO – Go to 'Working with tables'

15 I can work out averages.

YES – Go to question 16.
NO – Go to 'Repeated results'

16 I can organise results and record them in order in a table.

YES – Go to question 17.
NO – Go to 'Recording results in a table'

17 I can sort results.

YES – Go to question 18.
NO – Go to 'Sorting and recording results in a table'

18 I can draw a bar chart.

YES – Go to question 19.
NO – Go to 'Bar chart 1'

19 I can draw a line graph.

YES – Go to 'Practical work – results checklist'.
NO – Go to 'Line graph 1'

20 I can spot and describe a pattern shown on a graph.

YES – Go to question 21.
NO – Go to 'What do your results tell you?'

21 I can read data from a graph.

YES – Go to question 22.
NO – Go to 'Data analysis 1'

22 I can write a conclusion. It states what I found out and explains it as well.

YES – Go to question 23.
NO – Go to 'Discussing results'

23 I can write an evaluation. It explains why my experimental results are accurate and points out any errors.

YES – Go to 'Reliable results'
NO – Go to 'Was this the best way?'

24 I feel confident I can plan, carry out and report a scientific investigation to a high standard. Another pupil would be able to use my plan and get the same results.

YES – Well done!

What is the aim?

The aim of an experiment outlines what you are investigating.

Some examples of aims:

1   In this experiment I aim to find out how much acid is needed to neutralise a known volume of alkali.

2   In this investigation I aim to find out how temperature affects the speed at which the reaction between acid and alkali takes place.

3   In this practical work I aim to find out which is the best insulating material for a cup of coffee.

4   In this experiment I aim to find out which metals can displace others from their solutions (to observe displacement reactions).

What is the question you are trying to answer? For example, which material stops the most heat being lost (thermal energy transferred) from a cup of hot water? Changing this into a statement gives you an aim – 'In this experiment I aim to find out …'

Your examples

Rearrange these boxes to make sensible aims for two experiments.

In this piece of practical work …

How increasing the force acting on an …

object

Affects the speed it travels at.

I aim to discover …

Temperature on the height a ball will bounce.

Find out the affect of increasing…

In this experiment I aim to …

Planning – method

Your aim has now given you a clear idea of what you want to find out. You can start planning an experiment that will do this. When you are next asked to plan an investigation use the information given in the example below to help you.

For this example, the pupil wrote the following aim: 'The aim of this experiment is to find out how the temperature of an acid affects the rate of the reaction.'

Now think of a practical way to investigate the science. What are you going to do? Plan each step – this is called a **method** or **procedure**; it's a bit like a recipe for the experiment.

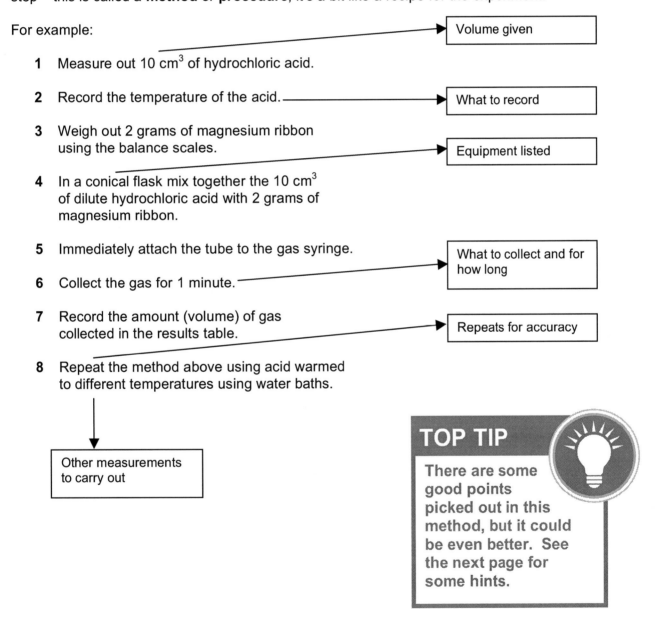

For example:

1   Measure out 10 cm^3 of hydrochloric acid. → Volume given

2   Record the temperature of the acid. → What to record

3   Weigh out 2 grams of magnesium ribbon using the balance scales. → Equipment listed

4   In a conical flask mix together the 10 cm^3 of dilute hydrochloric acid with 2 grams of magnesium ribbon.

5   Immediately attach the tube to the gas syringe.

6   Collect the gas for 1 minute. → What to collect and for how long

7   Record the amount (volume) of gas collected in the results table. → Repeats for accuracy

8   Repeat the method above using acid warmed to different temperatures using water baths.

→ Other measurements to carry out

TOP TIP

There are some good points picked out in this method, but it could be even better. See the next page for some hints.

Your method needs to include details and should answer the following questions:

1. What thing (independent variable) are you going to change (vary) in your investigation to see if it has an effect on the outcome of the results?

   How will you change it?

   > Example: In this experiment I am going to change the temperature of the acid. I will heat the acid in a water bath and use the following temperatures 30 °C, 40 °C, 50 °C, 60 °C, 70 °C.

2. What things are you going to observe and / or measure?

   > Example: I will collect the amount of gas produced for the first minute of the experiment. I will use the gas syringe for this and record the volume of gas collected.

3. What factors are you going to keep the same – to make it a fair test? How can you make sure they stay the same?

   > Example: To make this a fair test I need to keep these factors the same in the experiment:
   > - volume of acid used
   >   - 10 cm^3 measured in a measuring cylinder
   > - mass of magnesium used
   >   - 2g weighed on the balance
   > - time for collecting the gas
   >   - 1 minute measured with a stopclock

4. Is your plan healthy and safe? What have you done to make it healthy and safe? Check with your teacher before you start practical work.

TOP TIP

Imagine that you are trying to create a set of instructions that someone else can follow precisely – will they be able to get the same results as you? Did you give them enough information?

Science Skills

One more time!

When you are carrying out an investigation how do you know if the results you collect are accurate? Good scientists check their results by repeating the experiment. Many scientists say that a result is invalid if it can't be repeated. However, that doesn't mean you have to use every result you collect!

Part 1
In this example Sam recorded the length of time it took a toy car to slide down a ramp covered with different material. Highlight the results you would not use and give a reason.

Sam's results

Material on ramp	Car journey time (seconds)		
No material	11	10	10
Foil	12	16	11
Felt	13	12	13
Wax	16	22	10
Carpet	12	11	12

Reasons

_____

_____

_____

These out of place results can be noted and explained in the evaluation – see later.

Part 2
Aled aimed to find out if seeds germinate better in wet, moist or dry soil. He did the experiment using nine soil pots, three for each condition. Each pot had very different results. Suggest some reasons for this and what Aled could do next to make sure he can repeat the results accurately.

Reasons

_____

_____

_____

Suggestions

_____

_____

_____

6.9

Fair tests

Most of the experiments you do are ones where you are investigating the effect of one variable on another. These are 'fair test' investigations. There are other kinds of practical work where a fair test is not a useful or possible procedure, so do not try to apply a fair test where it is not sensible.

For a fair test, you need to make sure that you keep everything (that might affect the result) the same, except the variable you are investigating. This makes sure your results are valid. The things you need to keep the same or control are called control variables.

For each experiment put a ring around the things you need to control.

---

1 | **In this experiment a pupil aimed to measure the temperature rise when two chemicals (A and B) were mixed together.**

To make this a fair test I would keep these things the same.

Volume of solution A

Volume of solution B added to solution A

Time experiment started

Amount of oxygen present

Thermometer used

Size of conical flask

Amount of stirring

---

2 | **In this experiment a pupil aimed to find out how swimming affected heart rate.**

To make this a fair test I would keep these things the same.

The swimmer

Swimming stroke

Swimming outfit

Length of swim

Lifeguard

Time of swim

Cost of the swim

Time heart rate measured for

Where heart beat measured

6.10e

Fair tests

Most of the experiments you do are ones where you are investigating the effect of one variable on another. These are 'fair test' investigations. There are other kinds of practical work where a fair test is not a useful or possible procedure, so do not try to apply a fair test where it is not sensible.

For a fair test, you need to make sure that you keep everything (that might affect the result) the same, except the variable you are investigating. This makes sure your results are valid. The things you need to keep the same or control are called control variables.

For each experiment list the things you need to control.

1 **In this experiment a pupil aimed to measure the temperature rise when two chemicals (A and B) were mixed together.**

To make this a fair test I would keep these things the same.

2 **In this experiment a pupil aimed to find out how swimming affected heart rate.**

To make this a fair test I would keep these things the same.

3 **In this experiment a pupil aimed to investigate how changing the length of the pendulum on an old clock affected the rate of swing.**

To make this a fair test I would keep these things the same.

6.10h

Measuring accurately

In any experiment you need to choose the right piece of equipment or apparatus to measure the variables. It needs to be accurate and precise. The equipment needs to be precise enough for the job, for example a tape measure is great for measuring out a 100 metre race track but not precise enough for measuring the length of a leaf. The equipment needs to be calibrated accurately, that is the units must be marked at the correct intervals and match a standard measurement. You must read it accurately: exactly which mark on the instrument represents the value you are measuring?

Select the best piece of equipment / apparatus to measure each variable.
Match them up.

Time	Top-pan balance
Height	Newton scale
Mass	Thermometer
Length	Tape measure
Force	Stopwatch
Temperature	Ammeter
Volume of gas collected	Gas syringe
Weight	Metre ruler
Acidity of a solution	Measuring cylinder
Volume of water	Newton meter
Current	pH paper

6.11e

Measuring accurately

In any experiment you need to choose the right piece of equipment or apparatus to measure the variables. It needs to be accurate and precise. The equipment needs to be precise enough for the job, for example a tape measure is great for measuring out a 100 metre race track but not precise enough for measuring the length of a leaf. The equipment needs to be calibrated accurately, that is the units must be marked at the correct intervals and match a standard measurement. You must read it accurately: exactly which mark on the instrument represents the value you are measuring?

Suggest the right piece of equipment / apparatus to measure the following in an experiment. There may be more than one answer for each variable.

Time _____

Height _____

Mass _____

Length _____

Force _____

Temperature _____

Volume of gas collected _____

Weight _____

Acidity of a solution _____

Volume of water _____

Current _____

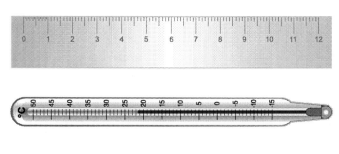

6.11h

The best equipment for the job

For any experiment you should try to use the equipment that would give you the most accurate and reliable results. Reliable results are ones that are believable and repeatable.

For each experiment pick the equipment that would give the most accurate results.

1 To measure the height of a small ramp.

- Metre ruler
- Measuring tape
- Protractor

2 To measure the current in an electrical circuit.

- Voltmeter
- Battery
- Ammeter

3 To measure the fastest runner in a 100-metre sprint race.

- Stopwatch
- Egg-timer
- Grandfather clock

4 To measure the force needed to pull a shoe along a path.

- Ruler
- Newton meter
- Scales

5 To measure the mass of a bag of sugar.

- Scales
- Newton meter
- Measuring cylinder

6 To measure a person's weight.

- Bathroom scales
- Newton meter
- Lab balance

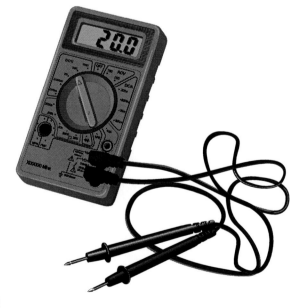

6.12   1/2

7 To measure the volume of a gas.

- Measuring cylinder
- Gas syringe
- Sealed beaker

8 To measure the temperature of a water bath.

- Water bath thermostat
- Thermometer
- Heat circuit

9 To measure the volume of the liquid in a small can of fizzy pop.

- 1 litre measuring cylinder
- 100 cm^3 measuring cylinder
- 10 cm^3 measuring cylinder

10 To measure the pH of lemon juice.

- Litmus indicator
- Universal Indicator
- Alkali indicator

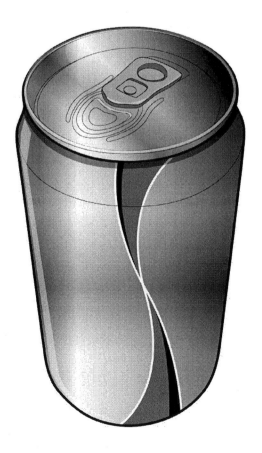

Drawing apparatus

Underneath your method you should try to include a list of apparatus and a diagram showing how the apparatus was set up for the experiment. This will help you to think through your plan and collect the apparatus you will need. If another pupil / scientist wants to repeat your experiment it also makes it a lot easier for them to follow your procedure.

Apparatus is always drawn in two dimensions (2D).

1   Always draw in pencil and use a ruler for all straight lines.

2   For a practical write-up draw your diagram of the apparatus set up for the main part of the experiment.

Draw the diagrams for the apparatus in the table below.

Beaker	Test tube	Boiling tube
Measuring cylinder	**Thermometer**	**Conical flask**
Filter funnel	**Tripod**	**Bunsen burner**

Gauze	Evaporating basin	Heat resistant mat

Clamp stand	An experiment set up

Experiment diagrams

As part of a practical write-up you need to draw a 2D diagram of the apparatus set up for the main part of the experiment. In the boxes below draw two diagrams of experiment apparatus as used in an investigation.

Checklist

☐ I have used the right symbol for each piece of equipment.

☐ The apparatus is labelled.

☐ I have drawn and labelled in pencil, using a ruler to draw straight lines.

6.14

Predicting

Whenever you do some practical work you will probably already have an idea of what you expect to happen based on the science you have been learning about. This is good because it helps you to set up a sensible experiment. However, you still don't know what will happen and every scientist should be careful about this and open to interpreting data in different ways.

Try to predict what you think will happen in each of the experiments below. To do this, consider what will happen to the dependent variable when you change the independent variable. What sort of pattern do you expect? The first one has been done for you.

1   A pupil investigated the effect of increased temperature on the reaction between weak hydrochloric acid and zinc.

As the temperature (independent variable) increases I think the reaction will get faster. I will know if it does because more hydrogen gas will be produced.

Reason: This happens because increasing the temperature transfers more kinetic energy to the particles. They move around more quickly and bump into each other more often causing more reaction.

TOP TIP

This is a good prediction because the pupil states a pattern, and uses her scientific knowledge to explain it.

2   Cross out the incorrect words. (Easier)

A pupil investigated the effect of light intensity on the rate of photosynthesis. When plants photosynthesise they produce oxygen so the pupil planned to put the plant under water and measure the rate as the number of oxygen bubbles being produced per minute.

Prediction: As the light intensity **increases / decreases** I think that the number of bubbles produced will **increase / decrease**. **More / less** bubbles will mean the reaction is going **faster / slower**.

Reason: This happens because light is needed for **photosynthesis / respiration**. It makes the reaction go **faster / slower** and produce more **oxygen / carbon dioxide** and glucose. Plants do not carry out this reaction at **night / day** as the light intensity is too low.

TOP TIP

Remember, a prediction needs you to state how changing your chosen variable affects the outcome.

(Harder)

In the next examples you need to decide and state which 'condition' is being investigated.

3   A pupil investigated the conditions needed
    for an iron nail to go rusty.

Prediction: _____

_____

Reason: _____

_____

_____

4   A pupil used a model of test tubes containing hot water to model the huddling in penguins.
    She wanted to find out the best way to keep all the penguins warm.

Prediction: _____

_____

Reason: _____

_____

_____

Planning practice

You should now have lots of ideas about how to write or record an excellent planning section. Here's your chance to put all that into practice.

Write a plan for the following experiment. The aim has been done for you. Swap your plan with someone else – is theirs a good plan? Why?

Aim - In this investigation I aim to find out how changing the temperature of a rubber ball affects the height of its bounce.

Method

Fair test

Health and safety

Apparatus

Diagram

Prediction

Best laid plans!

Have you covered these points in your planning sections?

Checklist

- [ ] I have written an aim for the experiment.

- [ ] I have listed the equipment I will need, including any chemicals.

- [ ] I have noted any hazard symbols on these chemicals.

- [ ] I have selected the most accurate equipment or instruments for the job.

- [ ] I have drawn a diagram of the apparatus set up.

- [ ] I have written a step-by-step method or procedure explaining how I plan to carry out the experiment.

- [ ] I have explained how I will make this experiment a fair test.

- [ ] I have decided to do a trial run or it was not appropriate to carry out a trial run.

- [ ] I have decided on a range of readings and listed the ones I will be using.

- [ ] I have decided on suitable health and safety precautions

- [ ] I have decided how many readings to take for each value.

- [ ] I have made a prediction stating how changing my chosen variable might affect the outcome of the experiment. I have given a reason for my prediction using my scientific knowledge.

TOP TIP

Imagine you are planning an experiment for someone else to do – they have to get exactly the same results as you did. A good plan will contain detailed but to-the-point instructions.

6.17

It seems like a good plan!

Jason has written down a plan to carry out a scientific investigation, but is it any good? You are going to mark his work and explain how he could make it better.

First read Jason's plan. Then use the mark sheet to record the marks you would award him. In the feedback column write one or two short sentences about how Jason could improve – some have been done for you.

Investigating the energy content of different foods by Jason Barewski

Aim
In this experiment I aim to find out how much energy is stored in 1 gram of different foods.

Method / Plan
1 Using a top-pan balance or scales weigh out 1 gram of peanut.

2 Fix the peanut onto a mounted needle.

3 Set up a boiling tube containing water in a clamp.

4 Measure the temperature of the water.

5 Set the peanut alight and hold it underneath the boiling tube for 2 minutes.

6 After 2 minutes extinguish the burning peanut carefully on the heatproof mat.

7 Measure the temperature of the water again.

8 Test with 1 gram of other foods.

Fair test
I will make this a fair test by always using 1 gram of food and always holding it underneath the boiling tube to heat the water.

Apparatus

Heat-resistant mat

Mounted needle

Peanuts and other foods to test

Boiling tube

Clamp stand and clamp

Matches

Equipment diagram

Prediction

I am going to look at the nutritional information on the food package and predict that foods that contain a high fat content will make the water get hottest, fastest.

Example results table

Food type	Water temperature at end
Peanut	

Mark sheet

Investigating the energy content of different foods

Question	Maximum marks you can award	Marks awarded	Feedback
Aim			
Is there an aim?	1	1	Aim given
Does the aim outline what the pupil is investigating?	2		
Method / Procedure			
Is there a clear method / procedure?	1		
Do you know the mass / volume etc. of chemicals to be used?	2		
Do you know what to measure and when?	2		
Do you know what to test?	2		
Are the results repeated?	2		
Is the method accurate?	3		
Is this a fair test?	4	1	Peanut needs to be held the same distance from the water each time etc.
Have any chemical and other hazards been identified and suitable precautions suggested?	2		Hint: Think about nut allergies.
Do you know how to record the results?	1		
Apparatus and diagram			
Is there an apparatus list?	1		
Does it list all the equipment needed, including any safety devices?	2		
Is this the most appropriate equipment for this experiment?	1		
Is there an equipment diagram?	1		
Is the diagram useful and would it really help you to set up the experiment?	2		
Prediction			
Is there a prediction?	1		
Does the prediction state the effects of changing the independent variable on the outcome of the experiment?	2		
Is the prediction scientific?	2		
TOTAL			

Note: If the answer to any question is 'no' you should award 0 points.

Reading measurements – liquid volume

Collecting results requires accuracy otherwise your practical work is not valid. Over the next four pages think about how to collect the best data and how to check it as well as practicing reading some measurements from equipment that should be familiar to you.

The volume of a liquid in a measuring cylinder is read at the bottom of the meniscus.

The unit for liquid volume is cubic centimetres, cm³.

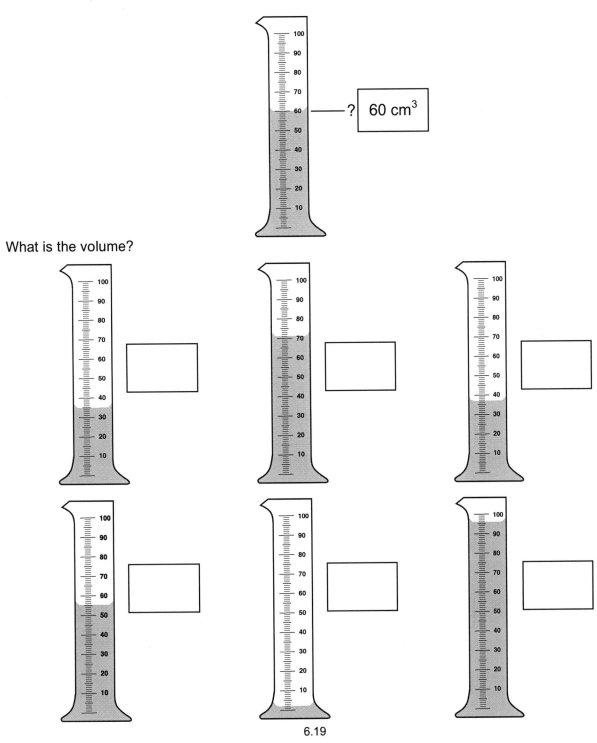

What is the volume?

6.19

Reading measurements – temperature

Temperature can be measured using a standard thermometer or a digital thermometer. The unit for temperature is °C (degrees Celsius).

1 What is the temperature?

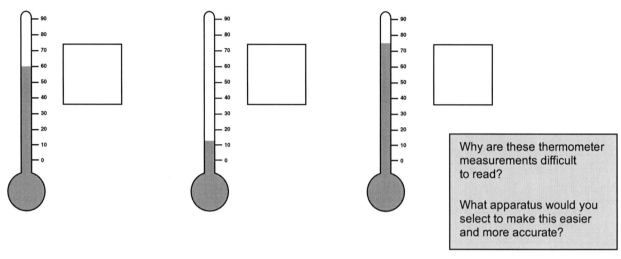

Why are these thermometer measurements difficult to read?

What apparatus would you select to make this easier and more accurate?

2 Draw in the liquid inside the thermometer for these temperatures.

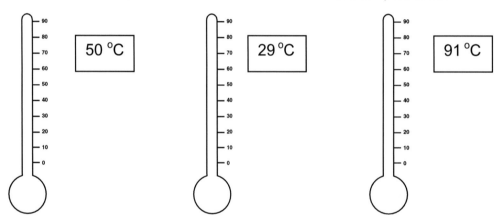

50 °C   29 °C   91 °C

3 Draw a thermometer that could measure from –10 °C to +100 °C.

4 Why is the thermometer in question 1 not good enough for measuring the temperature of boiling water? _____

_____

Reading measurements – length

What is the length of these objects? Pick the best piece of equipment for each of the measurements and measure the items.

1   The pencil on the left hand side of this page. Answer in millimetres.

2   The height of your exercise book. Answer in centimetres.

3   The width of a piece of A4 paper. Answer in millimetres.

4   Your longest finger.

5   The height of the door.

6   The length of the desk you are sitting at.

7   From one end of the room to the other.

8   From your school to the nearest capital city – if you're in a capital city, the nearest city to you. This might take a bit of research!

Consider the best units for each answer. Which will be most precise? How much accuracy is needed?

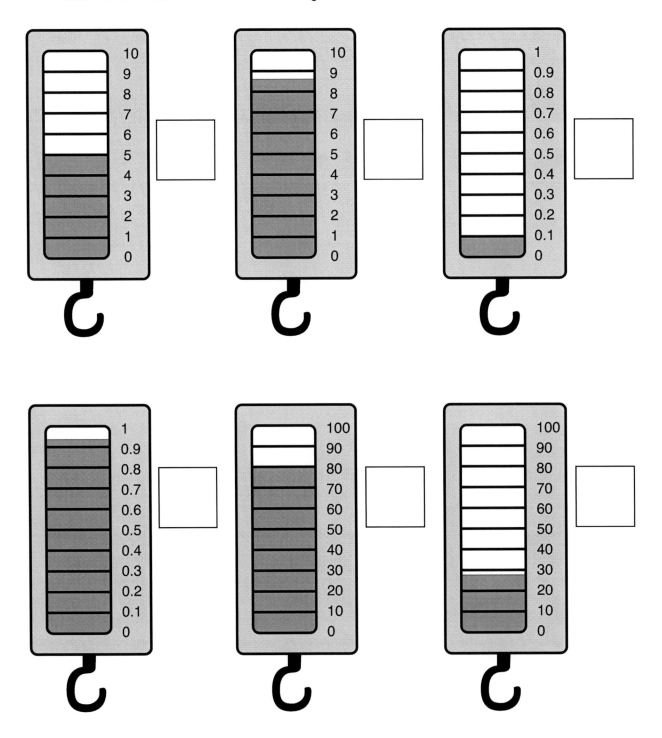

Science Skills

Reading measurements – force

A newton meter is used to measure force. The unit of force is the Newton (N).

How much force is each newton meter reading?

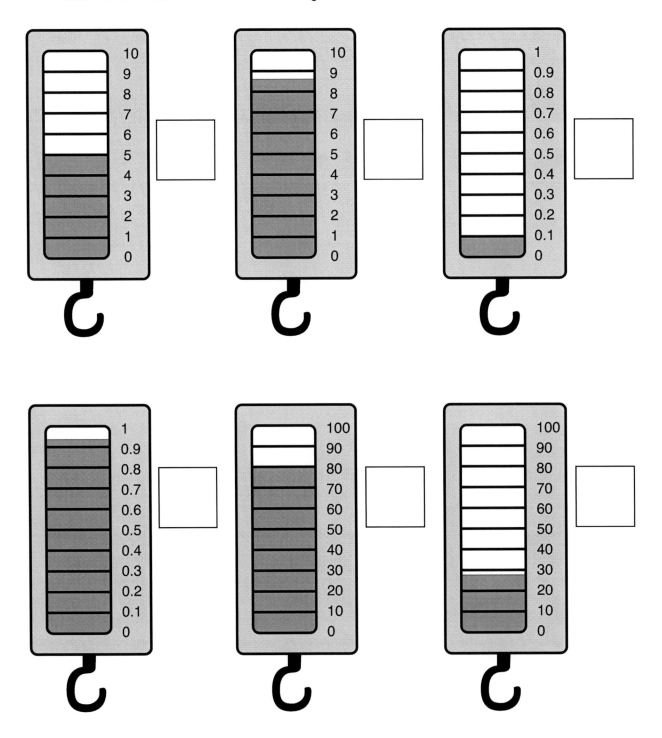

6.22

What is the best way to present my results?

Presenting your results clearly makes them easy to read and interpret.

Look at the experiments and decide the best way to present the results. Put a tick in the right columns.

Experiment	Written observations	Table	Bar chart	Line graph
1 Measuring the temperature drop of boiled water over ten minutes.				
2 Recording how many pupils can roll their tongue in your class.				
3 Investigating which colour jelly baby melts most easily.				
4 Observing the colour changes of Universal Indicator in different solutions.				
5 Looking at the effect of the thickness of a wire on the current passing through it.				
6 Estimating the number of dandelions on the playing field, using a quadrat.				
7 Recording how long it takes the heart beat to return to normal after exercise				
8 Investigating the volume of hydrogen gas released at different temperatures from the reaction between a metal and a weak acid.				
9 Investigating the effect of concentration on the rate of a reaction.				

TOP TIP

If you have two sets of numerical data you can draw a line graph. If you have only one set of numerical data you can draw a bar chart instead.

Science Skills

Working with tables

Tables can help to organise data. They usually have columns with headings and rows, but not always. In fact there is a whole variety of ways in which data can be displayed in a table. Just for a minute stop and think about how to describe a table!

For each of the tables on this page suggest a title – compare your suggestions with some given by other people in the class. Which are the best ones? Why?

Table 1 – New title _____

Sprinter's name	Race position
Billy Whizz	1
Frank Jones	2
Sarah Earhart	3
Arno Block	4
Luca Brown	5

Table 2 – New title _____

Age of apple (days)	Amount of vitamin C present (% of fresh value)		
	Apple type 1	Apple type 2	Apple type 3
fresh	100	100	100
2 days	98	95	95
7 days	97	92	60
14 days	95	86	20
21 days	92	81	2

Table 3 – New title _____

Parameter	Measurements					
Light level (%)	100.00	80.00	60.00	40.00	20.00	0.00
Temperature ($^{\circ}$C)	80.00	40.00	30.00	20.00	10.00	0.00
CO_2 level (%)	0.03	0.03	0.01	0.00	0.00	0.00
Rate of photosynthesis (%)	0.00	40.00	20.00	10.00	3.00	0.00

There are no wrong answers. What sort of title do you think a table needs?

Repeated results

In most of your experiments you will repeat the method to collect more than one set of results for the same variable and to check your accuracy. You should always hand in your raw data but you need to find out an average result that you can use when you plot a graph to show the pattern in the results.

Working out averages

In this experiment only one type of apple was used and its freshness, in terms of vitamin C, was measured at different times over three weeks. These are the results.

Age of apple (days)	Amount of vitamin C present (% of that in fresh apple)			
	1	2	3	Average
0 – fresh	100	100	100	100
2	**95**	**94**	**97**	
7	92	93	91	
14	86	84	83	
21	81	80	80	

To work out the average

Check there are no really out of place results that you don't want to use. It is useful to highlight these.

To work out the average freshness for the day 2 apples, add up the three values (shown in **bold**) and divide by the number of values.

$$\text{Average for day 2 apples} = \frac{95 + 94 + 97}{3} = \frac{286}{3} = 95.33\%$$

Remember to include units.

Work out the averages for the other three measurements.

Recording results in a table

A simple but effective and easy to use results table will usually record the value of the variable you changed (the independent variable) in the first column against the one you measured (the dependent variable) in the second column. This makes the information clearer and easier to use.

Write the results from this experiment into the table below.

A pupil dropped a rubber ball from different heights and measured how high it bounced on the first bounce. When the ball was dropped from a height of 10 cm it bounced 2 cm. The pupil dropped the ball from 40 cm and it bounced 12 cm, and from 70 cm the ball bounced 24 cm. When dropped from 1 metre the ball bounced 50 cm.

Height ball dropped from (cm) (Independent variable)	Height ball bounced (cm) (Dependent variable)

TOP TIP

Remember to include the units in the top line of the results table.

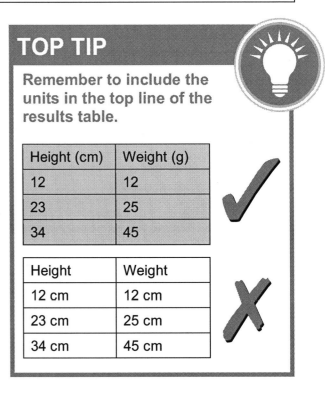

Height (cm)	Weight (g)
12	12
23	25
34	45

Height	Weight
12 cm	12 cm
23 cm	25 cm
34 cm	45 cm

6.26e

Recording results in a table

Putting data into a table may help you to see a pattern – see how much clearer the information is in the example below once you have completed it.

Write the results from this experiment into the table below.

The experiment investigated the effect of temperature on enzyme activity. At 0 °C there was no enzyme activity. At 10 °C the enzyme produced 1 gram of product. At 20 °C this doubled to 2 g. At 30 °C the enzyme produced 6 g of product, and at 35 °C it produced 15 g. At 40 °C there was a sudden drop to only 5 g of product and at 45 °C the reaction stopped.

TOP TIP

The first column should contain the variable you manipulated (the independent variable); in this case temperature. Don't forget to include units.

Sorting and recording results in a table

Organising data makes it easier to use. What is the best way to do this?

A group of pupils repeated their experiment three times to make sure the data they collected were accurate. They were investigating the effect of temperature on enzyme activity and took three readings for each temperature.

Design and record the results in a table. Include a column for the average result. You should complete the 'average' column.

Results

0 °C   0 g, 0 g, 0 g

10 °C   1.0 g, 3.0 g, 1.5 g

20 °C   2.5 g, 3.0 g, 1.0 g

30 °C   11 g, 6 g, 7 g

35 °C   17 g, 15 g, 26 g

40 °C   5.5 g, 6.0 g, 4.0 g

50 °C   1.0 g, 0.0 g , 0.5 g

TOP TIP

If you have any result that is really out of place and does not fit the pattern you do not have to use it to calculate the average.

Reorganising tables

Sometimes a table will contain a lot of data but it is not organised in a way that you find useful or easy to use. Take 'Table Z' for example – at the moment it is organised alphabetically by the name of the zoo.

If you were asked to report on the zoo that was the best value for money based on the number of species and then the admission cost, how could you rearrange the data so it is easy to find the answer? Design and complete a table that will help you to answer this question.

Table Z

Zoo	Opening year	Size (acres)	Visitors per year	Adult admission price 2006	Number of animal species	Number of lemur species
Auckland Zoo, New Zealand	1922	15	500,000	$18	178	1
Berlin Zoo, Germany	1844	100	2,600,000	11 euros	1500	0
London Zoo, UK	1828	36	600,000	£14.50	650	1
Monkey Jungle, Miami, USA	1933	30	500,000	$25.95	400	0
Melbourne Zoo, Australia	1862	55	1,200,000	$22	460	Unknown
Metro Toronto Zoo, Canada	1888	710	1,200,000	$19	460	0
San Diego Zoo, California, USA	1915	100	1,000,000	$33	800	1
Twycross Zoo, UK	1963	40	450,000	£9	152	5

TOP TIP

You can re-order information in any table to help you work with the data more easily.

Bar chart 1

When you have only one set of numerical data you can draw a bar chart to show the information more clearly. This is a skill you are familiar with and can practice on the next two worksheets.

Plot this data on a bar chart.

| | Number of cars of different colours in the car park | | | | |
	Red	White	Blue	Silver	Black
Number of cars	17	28	12	23	10

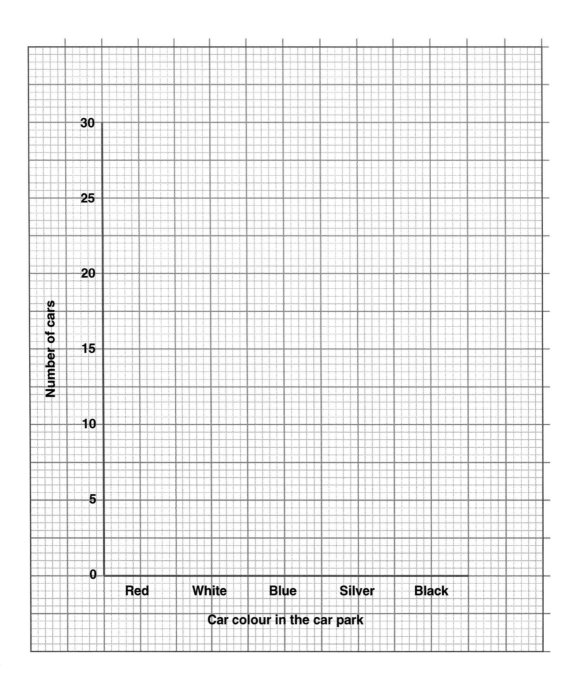

6.29e

Bar chart 1

When you have only one set of numerical data you can draw a bar chart to show the information more clearly. This is a skill you are familiar with and can practice on the next two worksheets. Plot this data on a bar chart. You may find it helpful to organise the data into a results table first.

In a group of 90 cars there were only five different colours. The most popular colour was white with 28 cars. Of the rest 23 were silver, 10 were black, 17 were red and the remainder were painted blue.

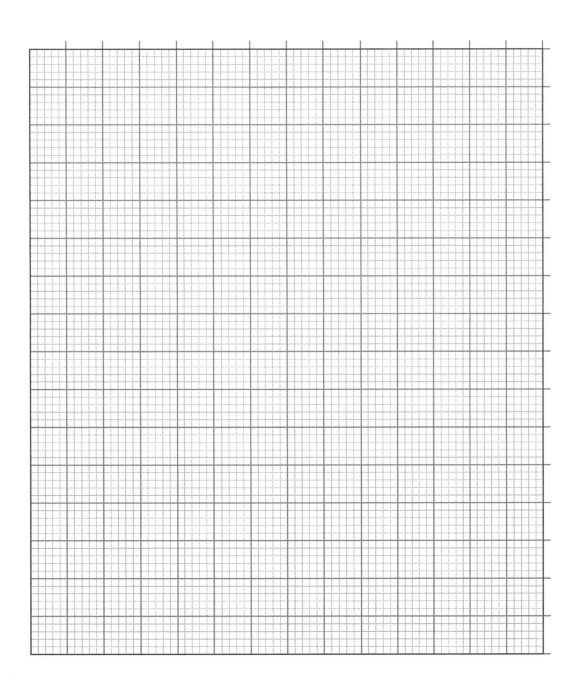

6.29h

Bar chart 2

Food packets give information about the nutrient content of the food.

Food (100 g)	Protein (g)	Carbohydrate (g)	Fat (g)
Wholemeal bread	11.2	37.1	1.7
Margarine	0.1	6.0	38.0
Kidney beans	6.9	15.0	0.6
Breakfast cereal	11.2	67.6	2.7

Plot the data on a bar chart. For each type of food plot the protein, carbohydrate and fat content.

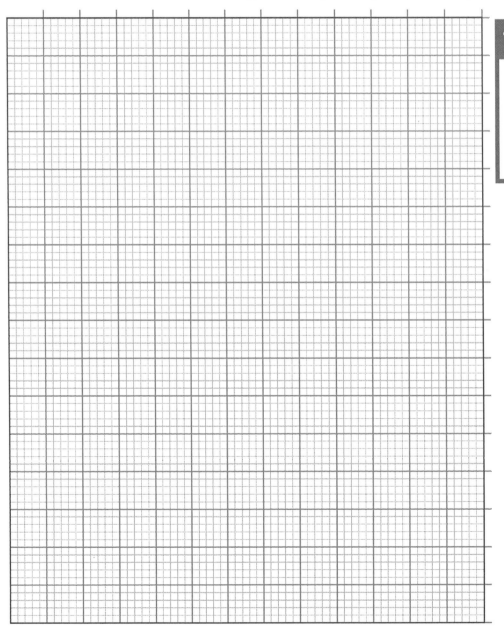

TOP TIP

If you are drawing a bar chart then you need only one set of numerical data.

6.30

Line graph 1

When two sets of numerical data are collected a line graph can be plotted. This will let you see a pattern more clearly. Use the skills you have already learnt to practice your line graph drawing.

A solution was gently heated until it boiled. The measurements shown in the table were collected.

Show the results on a line graph. Add the axis labels and include a line or curve of best fit.

Time (minutes)	Temperature (°C)
0	21
1	32
2	46
3	55
4	66
5	78
6	85
7	97

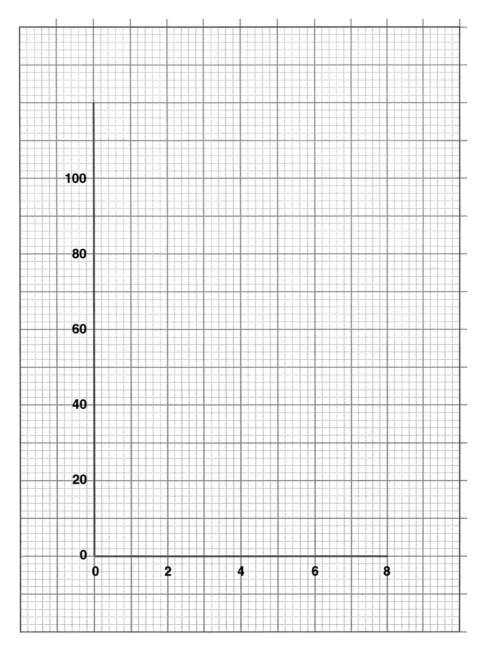

6.31e

Line graph 1

When two sets of numerical data are collected a line graph can be plotted. This will let you see a pattern more clearly. Use the skills you have already learnt to practice your line graph drawing.

A solution was gently heated until it boiled. The measurements shown in the table were collected.

Show the results on a line graph. Include a line or curve of best fit.

Time (minutes)	Temperature (°C)
0	21
1	32
2	46
3	55
4	66
5	78
6	85
7	97

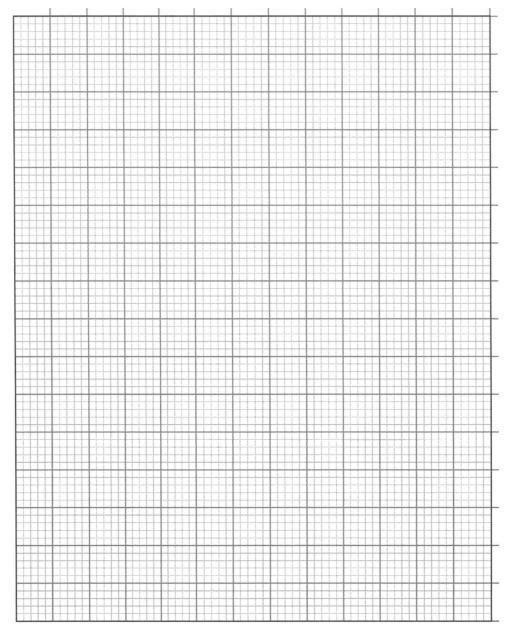

6.31h

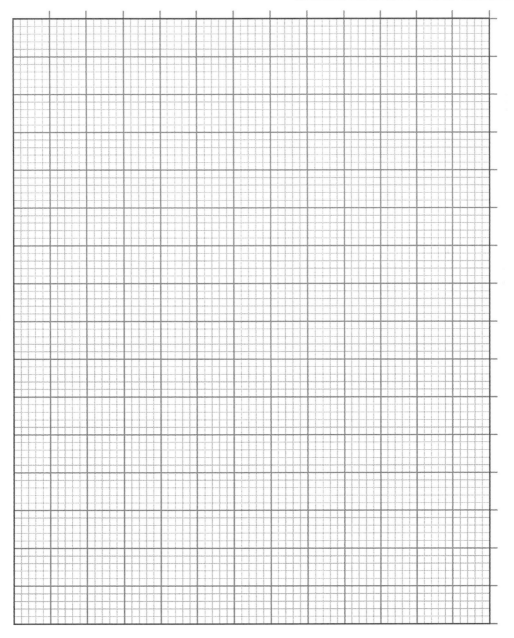

Science Skills

Line graph 2

A kind of mystery microbe was grown under controlled conditions in the laboratory.

The results shown in the table were collected.

Show the results on a line graph. Include a line or curve of best fit.

Time (minutes)	Number of microbe individuals
0	2
20	4
40	10
60	16
80	32
100	64
120	128
140	256

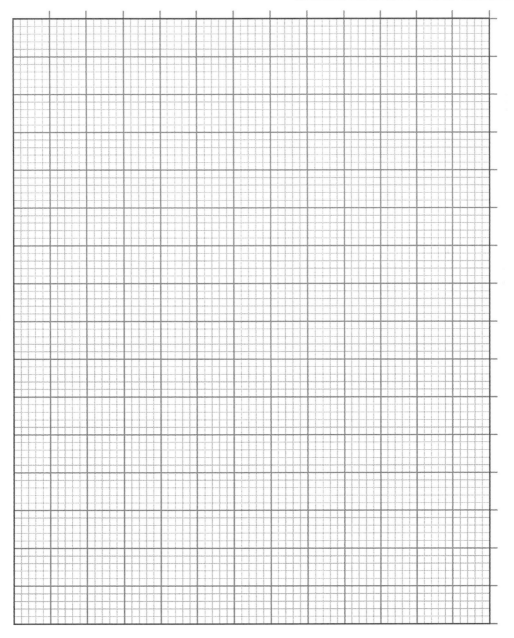

6.32

Results checklist

When you complete a results section use this checklist to make sure you get the best marks. The points listed here show you exactly the sort of thing your teacher is looking for.

☐ I have read measurements accurately using the best piece of available equipment.

☐ I have recorded my results in the best way.

☐ I have recorded numerical results in a table.

☐ The columns in the table have headings which include units.

☐ The data in the table is organised in a sensible manner.

☐ Any calculations I needed to do have been included and the working out shown.

☐ With one set of numerical data I have plotted a bar chart.

☐ With two sets of numerical data I have plotted a line graph.

☐ I have chosen the best way to present the data and I can explain why I chose this method.

What do your results tell you?

The conclusion section states any pattern found in the results and the scientific reason behind this pattern.

Once you have collected data and drawn a graph you need to look for a pattern. When the independent variable was increased or decreased what happened to the dependent variable? Some examples are shown below; these ideas will help you with the 'Looking for patterns' and 'Data analysis' worksheets.

1   Is there a pattern in your results? If so, can you explain it? Can you give a scientific reason for this pattern?

The effect of temperature on gas production

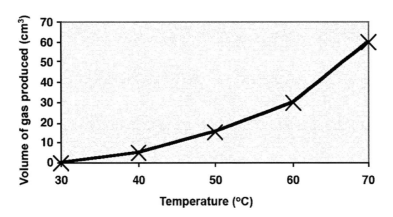

Example: From the graph you can see that as temperature increases so does the volume of gas produced.

This shows that as temperature increases so does the rate of reaction.

This is because _____

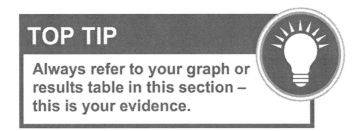

TOP TIP

Always refer to your graph or results table in this section – this is your evidence.

2   Do you need more results to make sure your conclusion is correct?

Example: The pattern I have found has evidence to support it between 30 °C and 70 °C. To test this pattern further I would need to test the reaction at other temperatures outside this range.

Looking for patterns

Spotting a pattern in the results you have collected will really help you to explain what is happening in an experiment.

Look back at 'What do your results tell you?' for extra help.

Describe the pattern in these graphs. Cross out the wrong words.

The effect of mass on spring extension

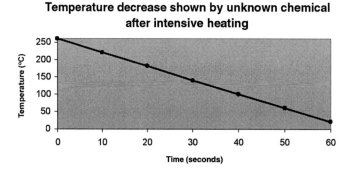

As the mass increases, the spring extension **increases / decreases / stays the same**.

Temperature decrease shown by unknown chemical after intensive heating

As the time **increases / decreases** the temperature **increases / decreases / stays the same**.

The effect of heating on an unknown compound

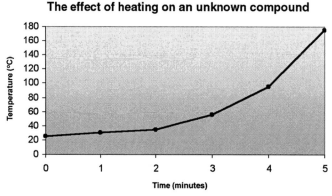

As the time increases the temperature **increases / decreases/ stays the same**. The change starts **slowly / quickly** and then **slows down / speeds up**.

6.35e

Looking for patterns

Spotting a pattern in the results you have collected will really help you to explain what is happening in an experiment.

Look back at 'What do your results tell you?' for extra help.

Describe the pattern in these graphs.

TOP TIP

Remember, the independent variable is always on the horizontal axis of the graph.

As the mass increases,

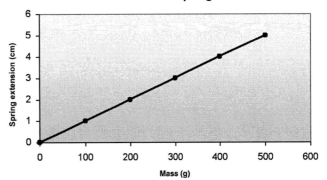

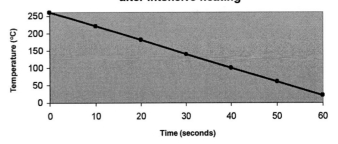

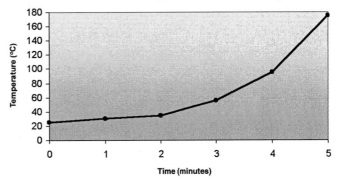

6.35h

Data analysis 1

Once you have drawn your graph you may need to read information from it to start writing your conclusion. The questions asked on the 'Data analysis' worksheets are the sort of questions you can ask yourself when carrying out your next experiment and conclusion. You can use the answers to help write the first part of a conclusion, which states any pattern found in the data.

These worksheets on data analysis will give you some practice at stating patterns you find in your data.

Answer the questions on the next page using information from the graph.

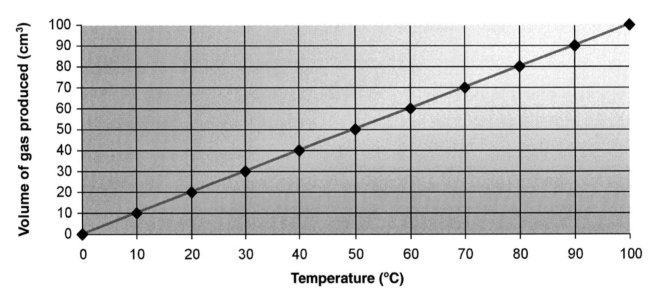

The effect of temperature on gas production in a reaction between hydrochloric acid and calcium carbonate

1   What is each division worth on the temperature axis?

    a 1 °C

    b 5 °C

    c 10 °C

    d 20 °C

2   What would be the next two values on the 'volume of gas' axis?

    a 105 and 110 °C

    b 110 and 120 °C

    c 110 and 115 °C

    d 115 and 125 °C

3   What kind of graph is this?

    a Line graph

    b Bar chart

    c Scatter graph

    d Pie chart

4   At 40 °C, how much gas is produced (don't forget units)?

    a 10 cm^3

    b 40 cm^3

    c 70 cm^3

    d 95 cm^3

5   At what temperature is 70 cm^3 of gas produced?

    a 7 °C

    b 17 °C

    c 47 °C

    d 70 °C

6   How much gas was given off between 50 °C and 100 °C?

    a 10 cm^3

    b 30 cm^3

    c 50 cm^3

    d 70 cm^3

Data analysis 2

Answer the questions using information from the graph.

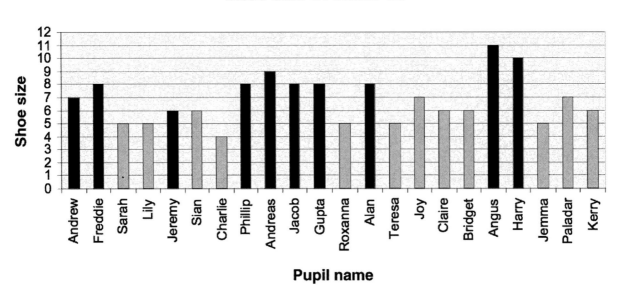

Shoe size of class 4B

1   What kind of graph is this?

| Line graph | Bar graph | Pie chart | Scatter graph |

2   What is Phillip's shoe size?

| Size 6 | Size 7 | Size 8 | Size 9 |

3   How many people have size 8 shoes?

| 5 | 4 | 3 | 1 |

4   Which person has the largest shoe size?

| Harry | Jemma | Freddie | Angus |

5   What is the difference between the dark and light bars?

| Small and large shoes | Boys and girls | Older and younger pupils | No difference |

6   How many people have taken part in this survey

| 18 | 20 | 22 | 24 |

6.37e

Data analysis 2

Shoe size of class 4B

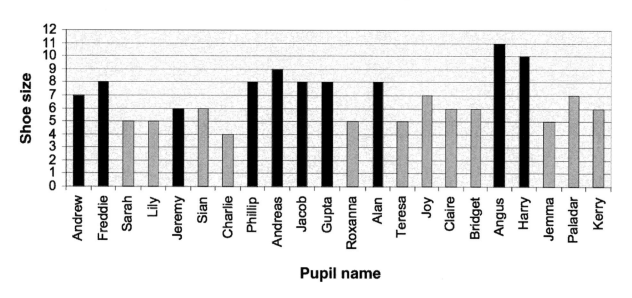

Answer the questions using information from the graph.

1 What kind of graph is this? _____

2 What is Phillip's shoe size? _____

3 How many people have size 8 shoes? _____

4 Which person has the largest shoe size? _____

5 What is the difference between the light and dark bars? _____

6 How many people have taken part in this survey? _____

6.37h

Data analysis 3

Answer the questions using information from the graph.

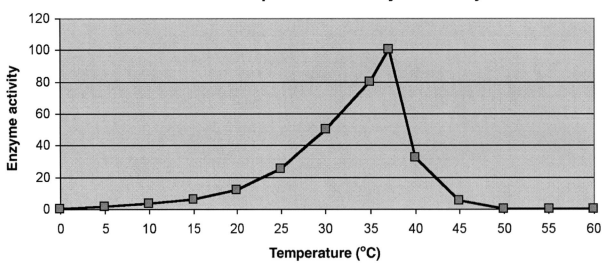

The effect of temperature on enzyme activity

1 What is incorrect about the 'Enzyme activity' axis?

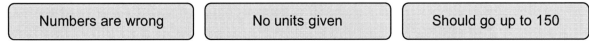

| Numbers are wrong | No units given | Should go up to 150 |

2 At 30 °C what is the enzyme activity?

| 30 | 40 | 50 | 60 |

3 At what temperature does enzyme activity peak?

| 32 °C | 37 °C | 45 °C | 51 °C |

4 At which temperatures is the enzyme inactive?

| 0 °C and 55 °C | 0 °C and 37 °C | 15 °C and 60 °C | 40 °C and 60 °C |

5 Describe the enzyme activity from 30 °C to 50 °C.

| Decreasing | Stays the same | Increasing |

6.38e

Data analysis 3

The effect of temperature on enzyme activity

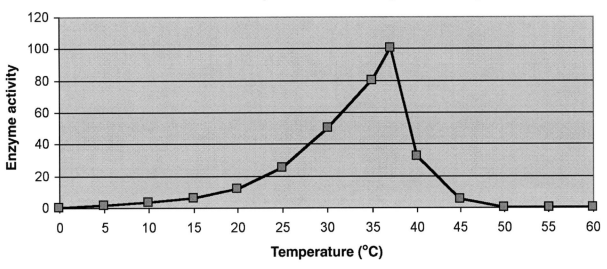

Answer the questions using information from the graph.

1   What type of graph is this? _____

2   What is incorrect about the 'Enzyme activity' axis? _____

3   At 30 °C what is the enzyme activity? _____

4   At what temperature does enzyme activity peak? _____

5   At which temperatures is the enzyme inactive? _____

6   Describe the enzyme activity from 40 °C to 50 °C. _____

7   What is the pattern shown by the line / curve of best fit?

    _____

    _____

8   Use the graph to suggest why it is essential to keep your internal body temperature at 37 °C.

    _____

    _____

TOP TIP

Remember to include units
for numerical answers.

6.38h

Data analysis 4

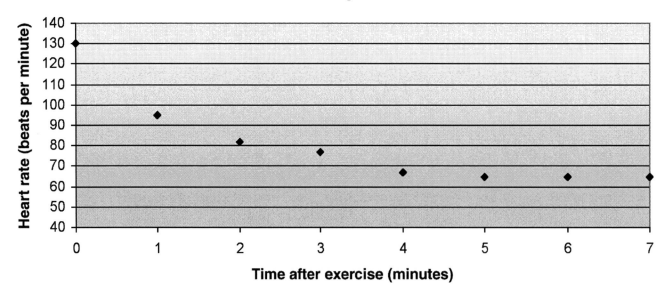

Heart rate recovery after exercise

Answer the questions using information from the graph.

1   Add a line of best fit.

2   For how long did the scientist record the heart rate? _____

3   What is the maximum heart rate? _____

4   What is this person's resting heart rate? _____

5   How long does it take the person to recover back to their normal heart rate?

    _____

6   Why do you think the rate of recovery is fastest between 0 and 1 minute?

    _____

7   What is the pattern shown by the line or curve of best fit?

    _____

    _____

Data analysis 5

Answer the questions using information from the graph.

% Food groups per flapjack

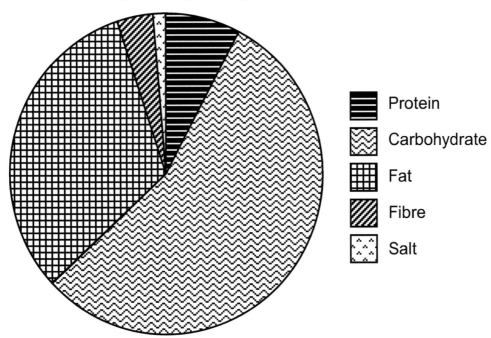

- ▬ Protein
- ▦ Carbohydrate
- ▦ Fat
- ▨ Fibre
- ⠿ Salt

1 What kind of graph is this?

| Bar chart | Line graph | Pie chart | Histogram |

2 Which is the biggest food group in the flapjack?

| Fibre | Protein | Fat | Carbohydrate |

3 Which is the smallest food group in the flapjack?

| Salt | Fibre | Fat | Protein |

4 How much fibre is present in the flapjack?

| About 5% | About 30% | About 50% | About 65% |

6.40e

Data analysis 5

Answer the questions using information from the graph.

% Food groups per flapjack

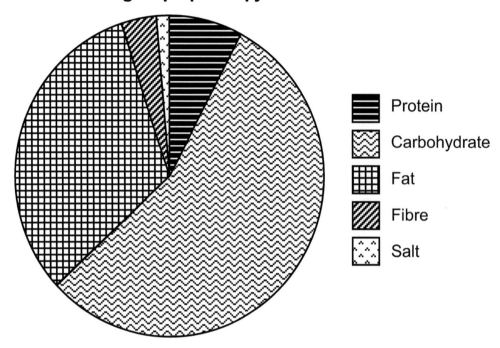

- Protein
- Carbohydrate
- Fat
- Fibre
- Salt

1 What kind of graph is this? _____

2 Which is the biggest food group in the flapjack? _____

3 Which is the smallest food group in the flapjack? _____

4 How much fibre is present in the flapjack? _____

5 What useful information does this kind of chart give you? What are its limitations?

_____

_____

6.40h

Data analysis 6

Answer the questions using information from the graph.

The effect of mass on spring extension

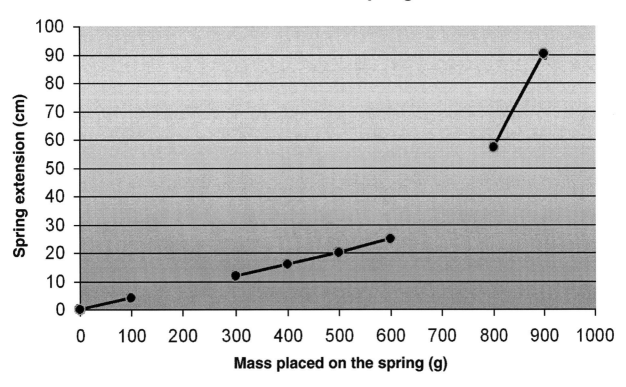

1 What is the maximum spring extension? _____

2 What mass is required to extend the spring by 58 cm? _____

3 Complete the line of best fit. What are the spring extension values for 200 g and 700 g?

   _____

4 What do you think happens to the spring when 900 g is loaded onto it?

   _____

5 What is the pattern seen in these results?

   _____

Discussing results

In this worksheet you are going to start putting together some of the skills you have been practicing so that you can write a full conclusion. The task reminds you of the sort of information to include in a conclusion.

> Maria investigated the effect of hydrochloric acid concentration on the reaction with calcium. She used 1 g of calcium in 10 cm^3 of dilute acid.
>
> hydrochloric acid + calcium → calcium chloride + hydrogen
>
> She collected the gas produced in a gas syringe for 2 minutes.
>
> The independent variable was acid concentration.

Results

Acid concentration (M)	Volume of gas produced (cm^3)			Average volume of gas collected (cm^3)
	Reading 1	Reading 2	Reading 3	
0.25	1	2	2	
0.50	6	5	7	
1.00	10	17	16	
2.00	25	29	27	

Task (Complete on the graph paper and lined paper on the next page)

1 Complete the average section of the table.

2 Plot a line graph of Acid concentration (M) against Average volume of gas (cm^3).

3 Write a conclusion.
  ✓ State the pattern seen on the graph.
  ✓ State what this means about the reaction.
  ✓ Use your science to explain the pattern.

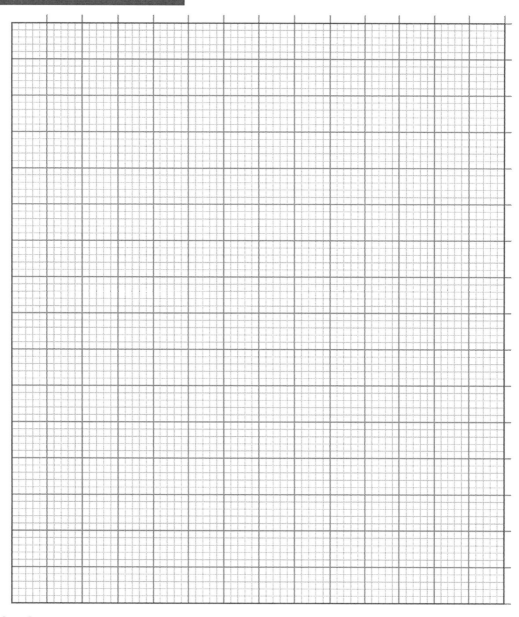

Conclusion

_____

_____

_____

_____

_____

_____

_____

_____

_____

_____

_____

Conclusion checklist

☐ I have used my graph as evidence.

☐ I have written down the pattern shown in the results and made it clear how changing the independent variable affects the dependent variable.

☐ I have explained how I know this, i.e. I measured a greater volume of gas being produced, or more reactant was used up etc…

☐ I have used my scientific knowledge to suggest a reason for the observed pattern.

Was this the best way?

In an evaluation you review how you carried out an experiment and whether the method you used allowed you to collect accurate results. Below are the sort of evaluation questions you should ask yourself and some example answers from different experiments.

1   How could you improve your method?

    Example answer: I would improve my method by using more temperatures and use separate thermometers to check the temperatures of the water bath and acid.

2   How do you know that your results are accurate?

    Example answer: My results are accurate because all the points fit close to my line of best fit on the line graph.

3   Have you any 'odd', 'out of place' or anomalous results. If so, why do you think these occurred?

    Example answer: I do not have any odd results. However, I did repeat some early findings as the water bath I heated the acid in did not heat the acid fully.

4   How would you continue this investigation? What would you do next?

    Example answer: To continue I would like to use the same method to test different temperatures and also use sulphuric acid and nitric acid to see if you get the same patterns.

Reliable results

When you have finished an experiment you should consider if the data you collected is accurate. Use the information below to think about how you can do this.

Method

A group of pupils were investigating the rate of photosynthesis using pondweed. They knew that the plant would produce oxygen as it photosynthesised. They placed the pondweed under water and counted the number of bubbles it produced over five minutes. Once they had collected some base data the pupils investigated how many bubbles were produced at different light intensities.

Results

Light intensity as distance of lamp from plant (cm)	Number of bubbles per five minutes
1	1
5	30
10	42
15	24
20	39
25	11
30	3

Evaluation questions

1 Can you spot any out of place results?

      a 5 cm   **b** 10 cm   **c** 15 cm   **d** 20 cm

2 Do you think doing the experiment just once gives you accurate data? Give a reason.

    a Yes because _____

    b No because _____

3 There are some things the pupils could do to make sure their results are accurate and reliable. Tick the box next to the ones you would do.

    ☐ Repeat the measurement for each light intensity.

    ☐ Try the experiment with another piece of plant.

    ☐ Do the experiment at different temperatures.

    ☐ Make sure the distance from light to plant is measured accurately.

6.44e

Reliable results

When you have finished an experiment you should consider if the data you collected is accurate. Use the information below to think about how you can do this.

Method

A group of pupils were investigating the rate of photosynthesis using pondweed. They knew that the plant would produce oxygen as it photosynthesised. They placed the pondweed under water and counted the number of bubbles it produced over five minutes. Once they had collected some base data the pupils investigated how many bubbles were produced at different temperatures and in different light intensities.

Temperature (°C)	Number of bubbles per five minutes
20	6
25	10
30	14
35	22
40	18
45	3
50	0
55	0

Light intensity as distance of lamp from plant (cm)	Number of bubbles per five minutes
1	1
5	30
10	42
15	24
20	39
25	11
30	3

What is the pattern for temperature?
Do all the results fit the pattern?

_____

_____

_____

Can you spot any out of place results here?
Which one(s)?

_____

_____

_____

Do you think doing the experiment once means that the data is totally accurate and reliable?

_____

_____

_____

How could you improve the reliability of the collected results?

_____

_____

_____

_____

6.44h

Evaluating a method 1

Two pupils carried out an investigation into the number of ladybirds in the school environmental area at different times of the year.

Once a week, except during school holidays, they went to the environmental area and spent 30 minutes counting the ladybirds. They always looked in the same places and recorded their findings in a table.

The project started in September and finished the next July. In April their teacher taught them what ladybird larvae looked like – so the next time they went to the environmental area the pupils counted larvae and adult ladybirds.

Think carefully about the way this investigation was carried out. How could it be improved?

_____

_____

_____

_____

_____

_____

_____

_____

_____

_____

_____

_____

_____

Evaluating a method 2

Pupils were asked to investigate the effect of temperature on the reaction between sodium thiosulfate and hydrochloric acid. When these two chemicals react they go cloudy – timing this can give you data about the speed of the reaction. One pupil wrote this method.

1   Measure out 25 cm^3 of sodium thiosulfate and place it in a conical flask.

2   Add hydrochloric acid to it.

3   Start the stopwatch and time how long it takes for the solution to go cloudy.

4   Do the experiment again at different temperatures.

What improvements could you make to this plan to make sure the pupil collects accurate and reliable results?

_____

_____

_____

_____

_____

_____

_____

_____

_____

_____

_____

TOP TIP

A good method / plan gives you lots of details. Another pupil should be able to carry out the plan and get the same results that you did.

Practical work checklist

These are the criteria your teacher will use to mark each section of a practical report. You can check your own work against it and refer back to your worksheets where you need some extra help.

Planning

Ticklist	Criteria	Refer to these worksheets for help
	I have written an aim for the experiment.	What is the aim?
	I have listed the equipment I will need, including any chemicals.	The best equipment for the job
	I have noted any hazard symbols on these chemicals.	Hazard symbols Using hazard symbols
	I have selected the most accurate equipment / instruments for the job.	Measuring accurately The best equipment for the job
	I have drawn a diagram of the apparatus set up.	Drawing apparatus Equipment diagrams
	I have written a step-by-step method / procedure explaining how I plan to carry out the experiment including health and safety precautions.	Planning – method One more time!
	I have explained how I will make this experiment a fair test.	Fair tests
	I have decided to do a trial run / not to carry out a trial run.	Planning – method
	I have decided on a range of readings and listed the ones I will be using.	Planning – method
	I have decided how many readings to take for each value.	Planning – method
	I have made a prediction stating how changing my chosen variable might affect the outcome of the experiment. I have given a reason for my prediction using my scientific knowledge.	Predicting

Results

Ticklist	Criteria	Refer to these worksheets for help
	I have read measurements accurately using the best piece of available equipment.	Reading measurements – liquid volume, temperature, length, force
	I have recorded my results in the best way.	What is the best way to present my results?
	I have recorded numerical results in a table. - The columns in the table have headings that include units. - The data in the table is organised in a sensible manner.	Working with tables Recording results in a table Sorting and recording results in a table Reorganising tables
	Any calculations I needed to do have been included and the working out shown.	Repeated results
	With one set of numerical data I have plotted a bar chart.	Bar chart 1 Bar chart 2
	With two sets of numerical data I have plotted a line graph.	Line graph 1 Line graph 2
	I have chosen the best way to present the data and can explain why I chose this method.	What is the best way to present my results?

Conclusion

Ticklist	Criteria	Refer to these worksheets for help
	I have used my graph as evidence.	What do your results tell you?
	I have written down the pattern shown in the results and made it clear how changing the independent variable affects the dependent variable.	Looking for patterns Data analysis worksheets
	I have explained how I know this, i.e. I measured a greater volume of gas being produced, or more reactant was used up etc…	Discussing results
	I have used my scientific knowledge to suggest a reason for the observed pattern.	Discussing results

Science Skills

Evaluation

Ticklist	Criteria	Refer to these worksheets for help
	I have stated why my results are accurate.	Was this the best way?
	I have pointed out any anomalous, 'odd' results.	Reliable results
	I have listed any sources of error.	Reliable results
	I have suggested improvements to the plan.	Evaluating a method 1 and 2

Compounds and formulae

Teacher introduction

This section will help pupils to develop good practice and a set of skills and strategies for tackling some challenging aspects of science – naming compounds, writing word equations and dealing with formulae.

The worksheets help pupils to work on understanding the processes and reasons why equations and formulae are written in such a way. There is also the opportunity for pupils to work out word equations for general reactions involving acids. I have tried not to make the process too mechanical and have definitely found that feedback and practice are the keys to success for most pupils trying to master these skills.

Pupils would definitely benefit from an understanding of the Periodic Table, element names and symbols before moving onto these worksheets. However, there is a formative self-assessment task that pupils can carry out in order to find the best starting point for themselves and to individualise their learning.

To finish the section there is a final assessment task called 'Compounds and formulae – Assessment task', which will test all the skills pupils revise, build on or learn about in this section.

Self-assessment

Answer YES or NO to each of the statements. If you answer YES complete the examples or statement and move on to the next question.

1 I know what an element is.

YES – Go to question 2.
NO – Look at the 'Periodic Table of the elements'

An element is _____

2 I can give the chemical symbols of some well-known elements.

YES – Go to question 3.
NO – Find them out using the 'Periodic Table'

The symbol for sodium is _____

The symbol for iron is _____

The symbol for oxygen is _____

The symbol for mercury is _____

3 I can give the name of the element from its symbol.

YES – Go to question 4.
NO – Find them out using the 'Periodic Table'

N is the symbol for _____

Si is the symbol for _____

Cu is the symbol for _____

K is the symbol for _____

4 I can name the elements in a compound.

YES – Go to question 5.
NO – Go to 'Combined elements'

Potassium oxide contains _____

Silver chloride contains _____

Copper sulfide contains _____

Carbon monoxide contains _____

5   I know the name of the new compound formed
    when a metal reacts with a non-metal.

YES – Go to question 6.
NO – Go to 'Name that compound'

iron + chlorine → _____

copper + sulfur → _____

calcium + water → _____

6   I know which elements are found in a
    compound ending in -ate.

YES – Go to question 7.
NO – Go to 'Compounds
ending in -ate'

zinc nitrate contains _____

copper sulfate contains _____

7   I can complete word equations to summarise the
    reactions between acids and metals.

YES – Go to question 8.
NO – Go to 'Acid reactions 1'

hydrochloric acid + nickel → _____

sulfuric acid + calcium → _____

phosphoric acid + iron → _____

8   I can complete word equations to state the reactions
    between an acid and an alkali.

YES – Go to question 9.
NO – Go to 'Acid reactions 2'

hydrochloric acid + calcium hydroxide → _____

sulfuric acid + potassium hydroxide → _____

nitric acid + iron hydroxide → _____

Science Skills

9 I can write a word equation to describe the reaction between an acid and a carbonate.

YES – Go to 'Acid reactions – test yourself'
NO – Go to 'Acid reactions 3'

hydrochloric acid + iron carbonate → _____

sulfuric acid + calcium carbonate → _____

nitric acid + sodium carbonate → _____

10 I can work out a chemical formula for a compound.

YES – Go to 'Is this the right formula?'
NO – Go to 'Writing formulae'

The formula for sodium oxide is _____

The formula for copper sulfate is _____

The formula for zinc chloride is _____

11 I have answered 'YES' to all of the self-assessment questions.

YES – Go to 'Compounds and formulae – assessment task'

Combined elements

The name of a compound tells you the elements it is made up from. You can work out what they are by looking for the element's symbol and name on the Periodic Table.

Match the compound names to the elements found in them.

Remember each compound will match to at least two elements.

sodium oxide (Na_2O)

potassium sulfide (K_2S)

ammonia (NH_3)

water (H_2O)

sulfuric acid (H_2SO_4)

hydrochloric acid (HCl)

iron hydroxide ($Fe(OH)_2$)

sodium chloride (NaCl)

carbon dioxide (CO_2)

methane (CH_4)

silver nitrate ($AgNO_3$)

copper sulfate ($CuSO_4$)

hydrogen

sodium

iron

copper

potassium

silver

nitrogen

carbon

oxygen

chlorine

sulfur

7.3e

Combined elements

The name of a compound tells you the elements it is made up from. You can work out what they are by looking for the element's symbol and name on the Periodic Table.

Look at the formula for each compound and write down the elements it is made up from.

Compound name	Compound formula	Elements
sodium oxide	Na_2O	
potassium sulfide	K_2S	
copper sulfate	$CuSO_4$	
water	H_2O	
sulfuric acid	H_2SO_4	
hydrochloric acid	HCl	
ammonia	NH_3	
iron hydroxide	$Fe(OH)_2$	
magnesium carbonate	$Mg(CO_3)_2$	
sodium chloride	$NaCl$	
carbon dioxide	CO_2	
lithium fluoride	LiF	
calcium hydrogencarbonate	$Ca(HCO_3)_2$	
methane	CH_4	
silver nitrate	$AgNO_3$	

7.3h

Name that compound

When two or more elements chemically react a new compound is made with a new name. You can work out what it is called by following these rules.

Reactant 1	Reactant 2	Name of new compound	Example
metal e.g. iron	sulfur	metal sulfide	iron sulfide
metal e.g. sodium	oxygen	metal oxide	sodium oxide
metal e.g. copper	chlorine	metal chloride	copper chloride
metal e.g. calcium	water	metal hydroxide	calcium hydroxide

Reaction type 1 – metal + non-metal

The new compound has a two-part name:
Part 1 is the metal that was used.
Part 2 is the non-metal that was used but it changes its ending to **-ide**
For example,

chlorine becomes chloride
bromine becomes bromide.

Reaction type 2 – metal + water

The new compound is the name of the metal that was used, then hydroxide.
For example,

calcium + water → calcium hydroxide + hydrogen

Complete these equations and name the new compounds.

1   magnesium + chlorine → _____

2   zinc + oxygen → _____

3   aluminium + oxygen → _____

4   lead + chlorine → _____

5   potassium + iodine → _____

6   silver + iodine → _____

7   sodium + water → _____

Compound names – right or wrong?

Use your knowledge to mark Amanda's work on word equations – seen below.
Place a tick in the box if the equation is written correctly, a cross if it isn't. If you think the equation is wrong write it out correctly on the line beneath it.

1   magnesium + oxygen → magnesium oxide

_____

2   zinc + sulphur → zinc oxide

_____

3   copper + oxygen → copper sulfide

_____

4   sodium + chlorine → sodium chloride

_____

5   sodium + water → sodium hydroxide

_____

6   calcium + fluorine → calcium fluorine

_____

7   aluminium + oxygen → aluminium oxine

_____

8   lithium + water → lithium oxide

_____

9   copper + sulfur → copper sulfate

_____

10 iron + chlorine → iron chloride

_____

Compounds ending in -ate

Compounds ending in **-ate** tell you that oxygen is involved. Once you know this it is much easier to name the elements in such a compound. For example,

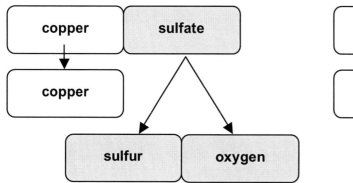

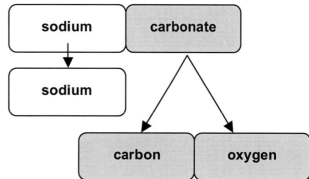

Which elements are found in these compounds?

_____

| zinc sulfate |

_____

| silver nitrate |

_____

| iron sulfate |

_____

| zinc carbonate |

_____

| copper nitrate |

_____

| lead phosphate |

_____

7.6

Name that compound again

Some elements stick together to make groups.

For example,

$$SO_4 = \text{sulfate}$$
$$NO_3 = \text{nitrate}$$
$$CO_3 = \text{carbonate}$$
$$PO_4 = \text{phosphate}$$
$$OH = \text{hydroxide}$$

Using the skills you have learnt so far, match the compound formula to its name.

CaF_2	silver nitrate
$LiCl$	potassium iodide
CuS	calcium hydroxide
FeO	lithium chloride
KI	calcium fluoride
PbO	magnesium sulfate
$MgSO_4$	sodium sulfate
$Ca(OH)_2$	iron oxide
$AgNO_3$	copper sulfide
Na_2SO_4	lead oxide

7.7e

Name that compound again

Some elements stick together to make groups.

For example,

$$SO_4 = \text{sulfate}$$
$$NO_3 = \text{nitrate}$$
$$CO_3 = \text{carbonate}$$
$$PO_4 = \text{phosphate}$$
$$OH = \text{hydroxide}$$

Using the skills you have learnt so far, try to give the right name to the compounds below.

Compound formula	Compound name
CaF_2	
$LiCl$	
CuS	
FeO	
KI	
PbO	
$MgSO_4$	
$Ca(OH)_2$	
$AgNO_3$	
$ZnCO_3$	
Na_2SO_4	

Don't let these numbers fool you – they are telling you about the number of atoms in each molecule.

TOP TIP

Each new element starts with a capital letter, but some elements stick together in groups, like sulfate, SO_4^-

7.7h

Acid reactions 1

Reactions between acids and metals

When a metal and an acid react two new products are formed – a salt and hydrogen gas.

acid + metal → salt + hydrogen

For example,

phosphoric acid + iron → iron phosphate + hydrogen

Remember

1 The first part of the salt's name comes from the metal.
2 The second part of the name depends on the acid that has been used.

Complete these word equations using the words in the boxes.

phosphoric acid + zinc → _____ + hydrogen

hydrochloric acid + _____ → magnesium _____ + hydrogen

sulfuric acid + zinc → _____ + _____

_____ acid + iron → iron chloride + hydrogen

_____ + lithium → lithium sulfate + hydrogen

_____ acid + _____ → zinc chloride + hydrogen

hydrochloric	magnesium chloride	hydrogen
zinc phosphate	zinc sulfate	hydrochloric
zinc	sulfuric acid	

Acid reactions 1

Acid reactions are common and used in many commercial and industrial processes.
Over the next three worksheets you are going to learn the general reactions for three different
types of acid reaction and then practice writing word equations.

Reactions between acids and metals

When a metal and an acid react two new products are formed – a salt and hydrogen gas.

acid + metal → salt + hydrogen

For example,

phosphoric acid + iron → iron phosphate + hydrogen

Remember

1   The first part of the salt's name comes from the metal.
2   The second part of the name depends on the acid that has been used.

Try these.

hydrochloric acid + iron → _____ + hydrogen

sulfuric acid + calcium → _____ + _____

_____ acid + iron → iron sulfate + hydrogen

_____ + lithium → lithium chloride + hydrogen

_____ acid + _____ → sodium chloride + hydrogen

calcium + _____ → _____ + _____

7.8h

Acid reactions 2

Reactions between acids and alkalis

When an acid reacts with an alkali (soluble base) two new products are formed.

acid + alkali → salt + water

For example,

sulfuric + copper → copper + water
acid   hydroxide   sulfate

Remember

1 The first part of the salt's name comes from the metal.
2 The second part of the name depends on the acid that was used.

Complete these reactions using words from the boxes.

sulphuric acid + sodium hydroxide → _____ + water

nitric acid + copper hydroxide → _____ + water

hydrochloric acid + calcium hydroxide → _____ + _____

sulfuric acid + _____ → iron sulfate + water

sulfuric acid + _____ → copper _____ + water

_____ + potassium hydroxide → _____ chloride + water

water	hydrochloric acid	copper hydroxide
copper sulfate	sodium sulfate	copper nitrate
calcium chloride	potassium	iron hydroxide

7.9e

Acid reactions 2

Reactions between acids and alkalis

When an acid reacts with an alkali (soluble base) two new products are formed.

acid + alkali → salt + water

For example,

sulfuric + copper → copper + water
acid   hydroxide   sulfate

Remember

1 The first part of the salt's name comes from the metal.
2 The second part of the name depends on the acid that was used.

Complete these reactions.

sulfuric acid + calcium hydroxide →_____ + water

nitric acid + iron hydroxide → _____ + water

hydrochloric acid + sodium hydroxide → _____ + _____

sulfuric acid + _____ → zinc sulfate + water

sulfuric acid + _____ → copper _____ + water

_____ acid + potassium hydroxide → _____ chloride + water

nitric _____ + _____ → zinc _____ + water

_____ + _____ → iron sulfate + _____

sulfuric acid + _____ → _____ + _____

Acid reactions 3

Reactions between acids and carbonates

When an acid reacts with a carbonate you will see fizzing – this is carbon dioxide being made. A salt and water are also formed.

acid + metal carbonate → salt + water + carbon dioxide

For example,

nitric acid + zinc carbonate → zinc nitrate + water + carbon dioxide

Remember

1 The first part of the salt's name comes from the metal.
2 The second part of the name depends on the acid that was used.

Complete these reactions using words from the boxes.

nitric acid + copper carbonate → _____

hydrochloric acid + iron carbonate → _____

sulfuric acid + calcium carbonate → _____

carbon dioxide	carbon dioxide	carbon dioxide
water	water	water
copper nitrate	iron chloride	calcium sulfate

7.10e

Acid reactions 3

Reactions between acids and carbonates

When an acid reacts with a carbonate you will see fizzing – this is carbon dioxide being made. A salt and water are also formed.

acid + metal carbonate → salt + water + carbon dioxide

For example,

nitric acid + zinc carbonate → zinc nitrate + water + carbon dioxide

Remember

1 The first part of the salt's name comes from the metal.
2 The second part of the name depends on the acid that was used.

Complete these reactions.

nitric acid + zinc carbonate → zinc _____ + water + carbon dioxide

hydrochloric acid + calcium carbonate → _____ + water + carbon dioxide

sulfuric acid + copper carbonate →_____ + _____ + _____

_____ + calcium carbonate → _____ chloride + carbon dioxide + _____

_____ + _____ carbonate →_____ + _____ + _____

7.10h

Checklist – acid reactions

Before moving on take a moment to review and assess your learning.

If you are not sure about how to complete this type of word equation ask your teacher or have another go at the worksheets.

You should be able to check off all the items on the list.

☐ I know what products are formed when an acid reacts with a metal.

☐ I know what products are formed when an acid reacts with an alkali.

☐ I know what products are formed when an acid reacts with a metal carbonate.

☐ I can work out the name of the salt formed when an acid reacts with a metal.

☐ I can work out the name of the salt formed when an acid reacts with an alkali.

☐ I can work out the name of the salt formed when an acid reacts with a metal carbonate.

☐ I know what causes the fizzing in a reaction between an acid and a metal carbonate.

☐ I know that a compound ending in -ate has oxygen in it.

Acid reactions – test yourself

Pick the right answers to fill in the gaps and complete the word equations. If you get stuck you can always refer back to the 'Acid reactions' worksheets in your Skills File.

Remember to look for the type of reactants, i.e. acid + metal or acid + alkali, to work out what type of products will be made.

1   hydrochloric acid + zinc → _____

2   calcium carbonate + hydrochloric acid → _____

3   iron + phosphoric acid → _____

4   sulfuric acid + sodium hydroxide → _____

5   hydrochloric acid + lithium hydroxide → _____

6   aluminium carbonate + nitric acid → _____

7   iron carbonate + sulfuric acid → _____

aluminium nitrate	zinc chloride	iron sulfate
lithium chloride	sodium sulfate	iron phosphate
calcium chloride	hydrogen	hydrogen
carbon dioxide	water	water
carbon dioxide	water	water
carbon dioxide	water	

Writing formulae

A chemical formula tells a scientist the number and type of atoms found in each molecule of a substance.

You are going to learn how to write chemical formulae, using the value or valency of each atom and chemical group of atoms. You will need to look at the Writing Formulae Data Sheet (sheet 2.18).

Example 1 Write the formula for sodium chloride

Sodium chloride (common salt) is a compound of sodium and chlorine atoms.
Sodium (in Group 1 of the Periodic Table) has a valency of + 1
Chlorine (in Group 7 of the Periodic Table) has a valency of - 1

We can show that these valencies balance by a see-saw diagram.

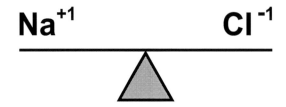

One sodium atom and one chlorine atom balance (by valency).
To write the chemical formula, leave out the + and - signs. Write the element symbols. As there is only one atom of each type there is no need to write number 1. The formula is NaCl

Example 2 Write the formula for calcium chloride

Calcium chloride is a compound of calcium and chlorine atoms.
Calcium (in Group 2 of the Periodic Table) has a valency of +2
Chlorine (in Group 7 of the Periodic Table) has a valency of -1

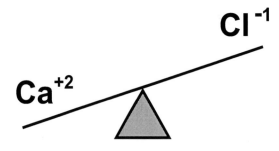

One calcium atom and one chlorine atom do not balance on the see-saw. What do you have to do to make the see-saw balance? You have to add another Cl⁻

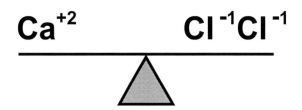

$$Ca^{+2} \qquad Cl^{-1}Cl^{-1}$$

To write the chemical formula, leave out the + and – signs. Write down the element symbols and number of atoms (except where there is only one atom of an element).

$CaCl_2$ The 2 is telling you that there are two chlorine atoms in the molecule

> Note: The see-saw is a model to help you work out the balance of valencies. It does NOT represent the mass or weight of the atoms. In some compounds the + and - symbols also correspond to electrical charges on ions, but this does not apply to all compounds.

Example 3 Write the chemical formula of sodium oxide

1. Find the symbol and valency for each element
      sodium: Na valency +1 . Na^{+1}
      oxygen: O valency -2 O^{-2}

2. Count up and balance the + and - signs
      Na^{+1} Na^{+1} balance O^{-2}

3. Write the chemical formula by leaving out the + and – signs and putting the number of each type of atom Na_2O

Example 4 Write the formula for calcium hydroxide

1. Find the symbol and valency for each element or chemical group of atoms
      calcium: Ca valency +2 Ca^{+2}
      hydroxide: (OH) valency -1 $(OH)^{-1}$

See the warning on sheet 2.18. Do not confuse Groups in the Periodic Table with chemical groups of atoms, such as the hydroxide group. To show that hydroxide is a chemical group you may put brackets around it.

2. Count up and balance the + and – signs
      Ca^{+2} is balanced by $(OH)^{-1}$ $(OH)^{-1}$

3. Write the formula, leaving out the + and - signs and any 1s
      $Ca(OH)_2$

Now try some yourself

Science Skills

Work out the formula for each of these compounds.

1 potassium chloride _____

2 magnesium oxide _____

3 iron oxide _____

4 copper chloride _____

5 sulphuric acid (hydrogen sulfate) _____

6 silver bromide _____

7 sodium hydroxide _____

8 zinc nitrate _____

9 copper carbonate _____

10 copper sulfate _____

11 potassium iodide _____

12 iron chloride _____

13 copper oxide _____

14 sodium carbonate _____

15 magnesium hydroxide _____

Is this the right formula?

Now you know how to work out chemical formulae can you say if the ones below are correct? Put a tick in the box if it is correct and a cross if it isn't.

If the formula is wrong try to write in the correct answer.

Compound name and formula	Is it right?	Correction – if needed
Copper oxide – CuO		
Potassium hydroxide – KOH		
Sodium carbonate – Na_2CO_3		
Magnesium hydroxide – $Mg(OH)_2$		
Potassium iodide – KI_2		
Aluminium sulfate – $Al_2(SO_4)_3$		
Methane – CH_4		
Calcium fluoride – $CaFl_2$		
Zinc chloride – $ZnCl$		
Lithium sulfate – $LiSO_4$		
Silver nitrate – $Ag(NO_3)_3$		
Sodium oxide – NaO		

Formula pick

In this exercise you are going to need to use all the skills and knowledge you have learnt in this section on formulae.

Can you put the right formula into the box for each compound name? Be careful – there are a lot of answers you don't need!

Copper chloride		Mg_2SO_4 $\quad$ Li_2S
Zinc nitrate		$CuCl_2$ $\quad$ KO
Magnesium sulfate		$MgSu$ $\quad$ K_2OH_4
Nickel oxide		$AlOH_3$ $\quad$ $CuSO_4$
Lithium sulfide		$Cu(NO_3)$ $\quad$ NiO
Sodium carbonate		$Cu(NO_3)_2$ $\quad$ FeS
Sodium chloride		$Zn(NO_3)_2$ $\quad$ $CuCl$
Potassium hydroxide		AL_3OH $\quad$ $C_6H_{12}O_{12}$
Methane		Cu_2SO_2 $\quad$ KOH
Glucose		Na_2CO_3 $\quad$ $ZnNO_3$
Magnesium sulfide		K_2O $\quad$ MgS
Copper sulfate		$NaOH$ $\quad$ $MgSO_4$
Copper nitrate		$NiOH$ $\quad$ $C_6H_{12}O_6$
Potassium oxide		$NaCl$ $\quad$ $NAOH$
		CH_4

Compounds and formulae – assessment task

Answer the questions below.

1   What are the names of these compounds?

    a Na_2O _____

    b Li_2S _____

    c $NiSO_4$ _____

    d $Mg(OH)_2$ _____

    e $FeCO_3$ _____

    f $Al_2(SO_4)_3$ _____

2   Complete these acid reaction word equations:

    a   phosphoric acid + magnesium → _____

    b   copper + sulfuric acid → _____

    c   hydrochloric acid + lithium hydroxide → _____

    d   copper carbonate + hydrochloric acid → _____

    e   sodium carbonate + nitric acid → _____

    f   sulfuric acid + calcium hydroxide → _____

3   What is the correct formula for each of these compounds?

    a   sodium carbonate   _____

    b   lithium oxide   _____

    c   copper nitrate   _____

    d   iron sulfate   _____

    e   iron sulfide   _____

    f   sodium fluoride   _____

    g   potassium hydroxide   _____

    h   aluminium carbonate   _____

Reviewing your answers

Once your answers have been marked review your learning and revisit sections you need a little more help with.

- For help with question 1 answers go to these pages – Combined elements, Name that compound, Compound names – right or wrong?, Compounds ending in -ate and Name that compound again.
- For help with question 2 answers go to these pages – Acid reactions 1, 2 and 3 and Acid reactions – test yourself.
- For help with question 3 answers go to these pages – Writing formulae, Is this the right formula? and Formula pick.

Science Skills:

 age 11–14

Certificate of achievement

Awarded to:

....

Signed .... Dated ....